WHO'S HURTING WHO?

Young people, self-harm and suicide

Helen Spandler

"Those of us in the 'tinkering trades' should look before we tinker."
(Maris, 1971: 123)

ACKNOWLEDGEMENTS

Special thanks to:

All the young people who participated in the research

Marion Lindsay — for management and supervision support

Bernard Davies — for external consultancy, and help with editing

Rachel Foakes — colleague and confidante

Alistair Cox — for help with the text

Janet Batsleer — for help in co-running the group discussions

Ross Grant and Elizabeth Battison — for administrative support

Also thanks to:

All workers and members of 42nd Street

Graham Hughes for allowing us to use his painting on the front cover

The 42nd Street Research Support Group

The National Self-Harm Network and the Bristol Crisis Service for Women — for their invaluable information and literature

Julie Farrand

Keith Green

Saira Weiner

Discourse Unit, Psychology Department, Manchester Metropolitan University

Stephen Raw for the cover design.

The research was funded by a grant from the Mental Health Task Force. Our thanks to them, and in particular to Tony Day for his support of our work. Our thanks also to Manchester Health Commission and Manchester Social Services Department for continued financial support for 42nd Street.

Published 1996.

Printed by MFP Design & Print, Longford Trading Estate,
Thomas Street, Stretford, Manchester M32 0JT

ISBN Number: 1 900782 00 6

CONTENTS

WHAT IS 42ND STREET

42nd STREET is an experienced and developing mental health service for young people aged fifteen to twenty-five who face wide and varied problems. These range from hospitalisation following breakdown; repeated suicide attempts; regular self-harm; stress; histories of violence; depression; isolation; physical, sexual and emotional abuse; and family conflicts.

It is recognised that statutory health and social services find it difficult to provide services for these young people — hence the urgent need for our service.

Over the last fifteen years 42nd Street has developed a wide range of innovative mental health work with young people in Manchester. We have offered a variety of individual support — befriending, counselling and informal support — alongside a range of groups based at the resource, and within the local community in collaboration with other agencies. We have initiated specific projects which include: preventive education work in schools and youth clubs; a lesbian, gay young men and bisexual mental health project; and community mental health work with young people in Salford and Trafford.

OBJECTIVES OF THE RESOURCE

- To plan services which offer an early intervention in the development of mental health problems.
- To provide support to those young people who are entering the community following institutional intervention.
- To respond to the views and needs of young people in ways that promote their sense of worth and importance.
- To provide education to young people and agencies about mental health, and to work towards reducing stigma associated with such issues.
- To promote self-help and advocacy.
- To identify ways of improving and providing a wide, innovatory and accessible service which relates to statutory services yet which still retains its voluntary perspective.
- To recognise volunteers' distinctive contribution to the work and life of the project.

These objectives are underpinned by a commitment to working towards equality of opportunity throughout the whole service.

FOREWORD
Who's Researching Who?

Who's talking — who's listening?

When perhaps the world's most famous woman says to twenty-three million television viewers: *I did inflict upon myself . . . I just hurt my arms and legs*, maybe just for a moment, that world stops to listen. And when she goes on to explain: *You have so much pain inside yourself that you try and hurt yourself on the outside because you want help*, maybe it even begins to <u>understand</u> a little better.

But why, you may ask, was this one woman able to command such an audience? How was it that she was able to raise such uncomfortable, even suppressed, images on the nation's television screens when so many others who could tell the same story have at best been ignored and at worst demonised?

Because, of course, this was Princess Diana talking. With all the authority of her self-proclaimed 'queen of hearts' role — though without quite being able to use the words — it was she who said that people do cut or burn themselves; and that, far from acting 'senselessly', they have some very good reasons for doing so.

It is messages like these which this book tries to get across and to support with evidence. They do not always make easy reading. Indeed, we need to know in advance that they may hit us very hard. Certainly, they may shake up our ideas. But they may also stir up our feelings and fundamentally question our practice. For what follows is a challenging account of how some young people — certainly not freaks nor even all that exceptional — <u>choose</u> to deal with the tensions which dominate their lives.

Who's telling?

Though almost too obvious to state, this book would not be worth publishing were it not for the words supplied by the young people. It is difficult, it is true, to envisage a better location than 42nd Street for such a piece of research. (As an outsider I think I am allowed to say that.) It has some of the best qualities of the voluntary organisation: clear about whose interests it exists to serve, very responsive to those interests, non-(indeed anti-) bureaucratic in its structure and self-critical in its working practices. By struggling to empower young people, including within the organisation itself, it thus manages to win the trust of many for whom rejection and exploitation, powerlessness and self-doubt are distinguishing features of their lives.

Helen Spandler, the researcher on this project, and the colleagues who supported her all worked impressively to hold onto these principles, in particular by adopting research 'strategies' and 'methodologies' which were remarkably compassionate and flexible.

In the end, though, it is the young people who emerge as by far the most compelling informants and teachers. They above all were clear-sighted about their often life threatening situations and behaviour. They were honest in facing these for themselves. And they were unrelentingly honest again in sharing their painful understandings, not only with a known researcher but — as they were well aware throughout — with an entirely unknown wider readership.

Who's learning . . .

In sharp contrast to all of this, my own role was marginal. As Helen Spandler's external consultant, I met with her for about two hours every month. I was also a member of the Research Steering Group which came together three or four times over the year the project ran.

Nonetheless, I now regard my contact with the project as one of my most important learning experiences. Much of this was very personal — and therefore provocative and uncomfortable. Slowly and uncertainly, it forced attitudes and assumptions out of the mists of the taken-for-granted and into a focus which demanded conscious attention.

As a former youth worker, I saw myself at the start as reasonably well disposed towards young people. Very quickly however I had to recognise just how unnerved I was by the traumas which these young people were surviving and the resultant emotional and sometimes physical scars. Often I was shocked and not a little repelled by what they saw as valid ways of dealing with their wounds. When I allowed my mind's eye images to take human shape — young people coolly taking blades to their skin, putting their fingers into naked flames, stepping in front of moving cars — I found them very hard to deal with. At that point — as it has done, professionally and personally, for at least four decades — my well-meaning liberal 'carer' persona unthinkingly took over. They must be helped, I immediately concluded. That is, they must be stopped.

And so perhaps they must be. For, as most of the young people who talked with the Researcher made clear, it is not good enough to say to them: 'If you think your way of doing things is better than ours, then get on with it'. They might be demanding a new respect for their definition of 'the problem', for their chosen 'solutions'. That does not mean that they want us — or that we who say we care can afford — just to shift our gaze.

This does not necessarily mean either, however, that the conventional 'liberal carer's' reactions are necessarily appropriate. Indeed, if this study shows anything, it is that this mind-set contains intrinsic flaws which, as a minimum, seriously impede basic communication between young person and would-be helper.

Such fault lines flow at least from the notion that an 'answer' — even perhaps the answer — is achievable. For, however liberal, few professional helpers can abandon the assumption that their interventions must bring some relief, some improvement, even perhaps a 'cure'. (Evidence that these may end up as part of 'the problem' is even less tolerable.)

Yet this study suggests that, without abandoning all expectation of 'doing (some) good', such caring approaches have to be seen as 'unfinished'. Their limitations stem not just from unfortunate technical failings in how we apply the wisdom and skill they put at our disposal. Rather, they are intrinsic to such essentially human enterprises — which are only marginally less flawed because they are called 'youth work' or 'counselling' or 'psychiatry'.

What therefore if others — perhaps especially those who experience and survive our interventions — define 'the problem' in a different way? What if they offer alternative proposals for ameliorating or resolving it? Are we then not bound to hear these open-mindedly? And, without assuming that in themselves they can determine the outcome, must we not purposefully bring such 'analysts' into the complex processes by which we construct our practice?

...and who's deciding?

The message in all this however is not just that, however professional we may be, we are not omniscient. It is also that we aren't omnipotent either. If no finally correct definition of the problem exists and if no-one has a premium on the wisdom or skill needed for improving human lives, then no one party within the helper-helped relationship can claim all rights to decide on these matters.

Given the realities of opportunity and resources in this society, serious imbalances within this relationship are probably inevitable. This need not mean however that such imbalances are non-negotiable or unchangeable and in particular that those who are to be helped cannot handle some of this power, especially over their own lives. Such attitudes do not only prevent us from hearing accurately what 'clients' or 'patients' say. Too often, they silence them.

In fact, with the appropriate professional and 'political' action, very different choices could be made, not only on what needs to be done — on 'treatment' and how it is carried out — but also on how we think, and especially on who defines 'the problem' and how. Imaginative developments of policy and practice become impossible only when those who already have the most power withdraw into their professional ghettos.

Who's researching?

To their credit, those responsible for carrying out this research were determined not to do this. They were particularly aware of the need to alter some key balances of power within the research process. Not surprisingly, we — for here I would certainly want to include myself — were not always clear initially just how to do this. After all this is a field which has been colonised by professional researchers — mainly academics working from high prestige educational institutions. It is they who usually decide what constitutes research, what count as valid findings, who can be seen as capable of interpreting these. Too often, it seems, research is what professional researchers do — and nothing else.

To protect this professional dominance, the 'objectivity' of certain (especially quantitative) methods has usually been most emphasised. Yet, such a stance ignores or denies one inescapable reality: that, when researching something like attempted suicide or self-harm, such objectivity is a myth. For, what this inevitably involves is one set of human beings confronting and then striving to understand the intentions and feelings of other human beings.

These same dominant professional wisdoms, by determining who comes to see themselves as capable of 'doing research', also effectively exclude a whole range of non-professionals who might, given the recognition, make no less valid a contribution. Such as, for example, 'clients' or patients, to say nothing of 'practitioners', whose systematic and self-reflective accounts and analyses of their experiences can do what 'professional' researchers claim to be their raison d'être: namely, work at the very boundaries of our current knowledge and understanding.

Very self-consciously, this project strove to discover the often startlingly different 'truths' which such 'de-colonised' research can provide. As Helen Spandler herself makes clear, the methodology needed for this kind of alternative strategy was not arrived at instantly, nor could it be applied in a wholly uncompromised form. She, like all of us negotiating such personal and professional change, sought it via an often demanding process of reflection, self-criticism and action. And this, significantly, would seem to have been pushed along fastest by her exchanges with young people.

What lessons for practice?

The radicalism of the 'findings' flowing from this attempt to rebalance the power relations within the research process certainly took me and I think others by surprise. The young people did much more than offer alternative definitions of the 'problem' of attempted suicide and self-harm. For them, at some levels of conscious choice, these were not only not a problem. They could be an important part of the solution.

Or again, the study highlighted just how high costly our interventions could be for the intended beneficiaries. Possible unintended consequences, it became clear, might be not just a further loss of control for the young people over their lives and so further damage to their pride, self-image and confidence. As their bottled-up emotions found their outlet, they could also expose the young people to greater risk of physical injury and to even more serious attempts to kill themselves.

Lessons like these are already having an impact on 42nd Street's work. Hopefully, through future publications, it will give some practice-based accounts of what this means for both policy and practice. At this stage I find myself able to contribute only rather abstract, and clichéd, formulations of such lessons to the rethinking which, this study shows, is now urgently needed. They include:

- A need to struggle harder to grasp, and then to start, where the young people actually are.
- A need to hear what they have to say in ways which allow it to influence our preconceptions about what's going on and our predilections on how to act.
- A need to remember that, whatever labels have been attached to them (not least the one of 'young'), young people have the right to be treated as responsible and autonomous human beings and not reduced to the object of someone else's intentions.
- A need therefore to trust what they are telling us until we have strong evidence on why we can no longer do so.
- A need to support and indeed embrace both the young people's individual strengths and their potential for collective action.
- A need to work even harder to understand how, within the given definitions and boundaries of our professional and organisational roles, we can release those strengths — by acting as a catalyst, enabler, resource person and so on.

Changes like these, in our personal consciousness, practice and policies are always difficult to achieve. However they would seem to be the very least we should expect of ourselves if we are genuinely to respect the often painful stories which, through this project, fifteen very resilient and very honest young people have shared with us.

BERNARD DAVIES
Research Consultant

INTRODUCTION
The Focus Of The Study

The research project reported in this book focussed on young people between the ages of fifteen and twenty-five who had repeatedly harmed themselves — that is, on three or more occasions — either by attempting suicide or through self-harm. Such behaviour was taken to include any form of self-harm, with or without suicidal intent, other than eating distress and drug use, although some of the young people included in the study might also have experienced these.

The ways of self-harming and attempting suicide which the young people disclosed in the individual interviews included :

- Cutting wrists including cutting arms, legs, throat and stomach (8).
- Overdosing (8).
- Banging head (3).
- Burning self — for example, with cigarettes (2).

Individual young people also talked about biting themselves; setting fire to themselves; driving a car into a wall; trying to hang themselves; eating glass; throwing themselves into a canal; jumping out of a window; throwing themselves in front of a car; and drinking bleach.

Though it was recognised that some very distinct differences may exist between the two behaviours, this research as far as possible sought to avoid preconceived ideas about the relationship between self-harm and attempted suicide or between each of these and suicidal intent. Indeed, in order to engage the young people in the research, an effort was made to in some way collapse the self-harm/attempted suicide distinction. Thus the criterion used for involving the young people was that they should have repeatedly either harmed themselves or attempted suicide. As with other key elements of the research, one important aim was to explore the relationship between suicide and self-harm by investigating the young people's own views, feelings and opinions on the differences between them. (See Chapter 2: 'The Next Best Thing'.)

Why a research project on attempted suicide and self-harm within 42nd Street?

42nd Street is a community mental health resource for young people aged fifteen to twenty-five who are facing a wide range of personal, emotional and psychological problems. Its responses include individual support — befriending, counselling and informal support — and a variety of groups based both within 42nd Street itself and in young people's own communities.

This research project was prompted by an awareness within 42nd Street that increasing numbers of young people seeking its support were disclosing suicide attempts and self-harm. An analysis of young people presenting at 42nd Street carried out as part of the research showed that between November 1994 — June 1995, of 120 young men and women making a first contact with the project, at their first meeting with a worker 45% disclosed attempted suicide, self-harm or both. 27% of this total disclosed attempts at suicide and/or self-harm on three or more occasions. As many young people were not asked the relevant questions and many others might well not have disclosed on first contact, these figures could well underestimate the extent of the problem.

In 1994, 42nd Street therefore applied for and was awarded funding by the Mental Health Task Force to undertake research into the needs and experiences of young people who attempt suicide and/or who self-harm. From August 1994 to August 1995, the research was carried out by a full-time research worker (Helen Spandler), culminating in a National Conference in Manchester in July 1995.

In response to the same concerns, in July 1994 42nd Street also established a three-year practice project with the aim of developing new ways of working with young people who attempt suicide and self-harm. By January 1995 this was providing a weekly outreach session at a local hospital accident and emergency department, a community based group, an evening telephone helpline and individual support to young people. At that stage future plans for this project included developing forms of group work to enable young people to explore self-harm and suicide and creating and producing information and resources for young people and for workers aimed at increasing their awareness and understanding. The project was also employing an Asian woman sessional worker to deal with the specific needs of Asian young women and to work with the other 42nd Street staff to initiate new ways of responding to their needs.

Research perspectives

Explicitly and unashamedly, this study set out to allow the voices of young people who attempt suicide and/or self-harm to come through as strongly as possible. In order to get the in-depth responses which were therefore needed in the time available to one researcher in one year, only small numbers of young people could be involved in the research processes.

The material for the research was thus gathered in two main ways:

- A series of in-depth interviews was carried out with ten young people. A gender balance of seven women and three men was deliberately chosen to reflect the approximately two-to-one ratio of women to men who were presenting at 42nd Street as having self-harmed or attempted suicide.

- Four group discussions were run each involving between two and four young people. A total of ten young people took part overall, five of whom had also been interviewed. These meetings also generated a variety of written and creative material.

A total of fifteen young people with recent and current direct experience of repeated self-harm and/or suicide attempts were thus involved in the research. Unlike much similar research, no control group was established — that is, for example, of young people who had not harmed themselves or attempted suicide. Moreover, if measured solely by the numbers who participated, this study was clearly very small. It therefore makes no attempt to draw broad generalisations from its material — for example, about cause and effect within the processes of attempting suicide and self-harming or about differences between young people who did and did not attempt suicide or self-harm.

Rather, from its inception the research was intended to be a qualitative study whose primary 'data' was specifically intended to be the views and perspectives of the young people themselves. Central to it was a commitment to investigate the complexity of meanings which they might attach to these activities — what they felt and thought about repeated attempted suicide and self-harm, how they made sense of their behaviour, how they understood and viewed its meaning and functions and how they judged service provision.

Like some other recent developments specifically concerned with self-harm (eg Arnold, 1995), it was thus a quite explicit attempt to go beyond medical and clinical approaches and definitions of the problem. The value of an approach based on 'listening to adolescents rather then reacting to them' was highlighted in a study of young female adolescents who 'carved' (cut) themselves.

> "We learned only after we were willing to concede that we did not understand the girls' behaviour, when we suspended our clinical judgement, when we grudgingly allowed the girls to explain their behaviour to us, and when we stopped playing expert and allowed ourselves to become students. The girls became our teachers." (Ross & McKay, 1979: 5)

Such an approach assumes a deliberate attempt to shift some of the balances of power which normally exist in the exchanges between researchers and their 'subjects' firmly in favour of the latter. A brief literature survey is therefore included for two main reasons: to outline something of the process through which this project sought to loosen itself from previous researchers' (and indeed practitioners') conventional wisdoms; and to place in context both the approaches it did adopt and the nature of its outcomes.

Attempted suicide and self-harm: some dominant perspectives and assumptions

The following account in a sense reflects the researcher's own thinking and development. While from the start the aim of the research was to explore young people's own perspectives, the researcher still started off exploring a fairly conventional research perspective, reading a lot of established literature. This was useful to give a background to the research and to reveal prevailing medical and social views about young people, self-harm and suicide. The researcher really began to break away from this after encountering writings by the Self-Harm Network and by Bristol Crisis Service for Women: the understandings gathered from these facilitated the move towards focussing on young people and what they themselves had to say. This process is briefly explored below.

A review of the relevant literature and observation of professional clinical responses suggests two distinct, though related, extreme types of reaction to young people who repeatedly attempt suicide or self-harm. These responses were also articulated and confirmed by the young people who participated in the research.

- One — 'therapeutic pessimism' or 'they can't be helped': one young woman for example described how she saw 'a failed case' written on her medical notes.

- Two — minimising the significance of the young person's self-harm or their attempt at suicide so that it is not taken seriously or is belittled: 'They don't really mean it'; 'Ignore it and it'll go away'.

Therapeutic pessimism

The first response is (apparently) related to the fact that repeated suicide attempts and self-harm are often seen clinically as 'symptoms' of a 'chronic personality disorder', a character pathology, or other 'flamboyant' conditions such as 'histrionic and narcissistic personality disorder' — or, alternatively, as symptomatic of a 'psychosis.' In particular, repeated self-wounding is regarded as one of the symptoms of borderline personality disorder in the Psychiatric Diagnostic and Statistical Manual, the official reference manual for psychiatric diagnosis. Traditionally young people, often women, are referred to as severely or chronically 'impaired' — for example, as 'chronic self-mutilators' (Favazza and Conterio, 1988: 19).

From a medical perspective, a 'chronic personality disorder' is usually regarded as untreatable, both psychiatrically and psycho-therapeutically. However, the validity and usefulness of the diagnosis has been criticised elsewhere (see for example Tantam and

Whittaker 1992; Lewis and Appleby, 1988). It has also recently been recognised that, once such a diagnosis has been made, further investigation into an individual's situation and the 'meanings' and 'functions' of their behaviour for them is likely to cease. (See for example, Tantam and Whittaker 1992.)

Little has been written specifically on young people who repeatedly self-harm. Rough estimates of repetition of self-poisoning by adolescents have been reported as occurring at a rate of between 10–30% of those who overdosed initially within one to five years (Goldacre and Hawton, 1985). Though not concentrating on young people specifically, a recent review of this area concluded that studies of intervention had not indicated any progress in reducing the risk of 'repeated parasuicide' so that the subject had been left 'surrounded by therapeutic pessimism'. Even when 'social stress has been reduced, the remaining difficulties appear to be too entrenched to improve, suggesting that parasuicidal behaviour is self-reinforcing' (Appleby and Warner, 1993: 15).

In particular, concern has been expressed recently over the difficulties faced by individuals who 'repeatedly' attempt suicide and/or 'deliberately self-harm'. In the context of an increasing likelihood of their eventually committing suicide, these difficulties, it is claimed, may be revealed in 'maladaptive' contact with the relevant services. This is seen to take the form of an overuse of available services or, contradictorily, of a refusal to accept help, particularly psychiatric help (Rygnestad 1988; Owens and House 1994).

A significant proportion of those who repeatedly attempt suicide have also been reported as being unemployed, socially isolated young men with a previous psychiatric history of frequent self-harming and attempting suicide with premeditation who have usually been diagnosed as personality disordered (Appleby and Warner, 1993). A corresponding increase in both suicide and 'non-fatal attempted suicide' has also been noted recently in the literature, and that the two phenomena could in some way be related. It could be therefore that the well documented rise in the young male suicide rate includes a large proportion of young men who have attempted suicide and or have self-harmed on a number of previous occasions.

Looking at young men who repeatedly self-harm and who also attempt suicide may help to illuminate why they have a higher suicide rate, revealing possible links between self-harm and suicide, which may in turn be relevant to other groups of people. However, concentrating on the male suicide rate has the risk of ignoring or belittling those, both male and female, who are in distress and who self-harm or attempt suicide but who do not actually kill themselves. It also simplifies gender differences in relation to suicide and self-harm, and leaves out other differences that may not yet be known about, as well as those that are known to exist. These include high suicide rates among Asian young women and among lesbian and gay young people.

A possible link has also been noted between self-harm and suicidal attempts involving self-poisoning and overdosing. Thus individuals who self-harm may be more likely to overdose (Favazza and Favazza, 1987) while those who have self-injured and self-poisoned may be more likely to repeat overdosing than people who have only self-poisoned (Tantam and Whittaker, 1992).

A number of assertions are commonly made in the literature about young people who repeatedly attempt suicide or self-harm. The most frequent is that they are 'manipulative' or 'attention seeking'. Others (Miller, 1994) stress that young women in particular are viewed in a number of stereotyped ways:

- as aggressive, unstable, unreliable, inadequate, and lacking in insight;
- as unable to form lasting relationships;
- as sexually provocative;
- with their 'sense of self' so damaged that therapy (for example) is unsuitable and doomed to fail, or will 'make them worse';
- as playing professionals off against each other;
- as failing to respond positively to psychiatric medication and as being difficult to manage and disruptive in groups.

It could be in fact that the repeated overdoser and chronic self-mutilator has taken the social and cultural 'space' previously occupied by the 'hysterical' personality who was usually seen as young and female and described as quarrelsome, determined and manipulative.

Minimalism

Along a continuum of responses, ones which minimise the difficulties associated with (especially) young people's repeated suicide attempts and self-harming stand at the opposite end to 'therapeutic pessimism'. These seem particularly to play down their distress and specifically their suicidal intent. These suggest a strong inclination to reject suicidal young people and particularly the ones who 'repeat' their behaviour, accusing them of a form of pretence by denying their desire to die. Little theoretical justification for this stance exists. On the contrary, as we have seen, the repetition of suicide attempts may increase the probability of an individual subsequently dying from suicide (Hawton and Catalon, 1987).

Nonetheless, in their day to day practice mental health and medical professionals may well tend to minimise the difficulties — by for example referring to the behaviour as attention-seeking or manipulative and by holding to a belief that 'they don't really mean it' or that 'they'll never actually do it'. This same attitude can be found in relation to self-harm which, regardless of whether it is or is not seen as symptomatic of a more general 'personality disorder' or of psychosis, may be dismissed as 'a phase — they'll grow out of it'; 'ignore it and it'll go away'. (See Chapter 6: 'Not A Clue').

At present, no doubt as a result of the well documented increase in suicide rates amongst young men, a strong interest seems to be developing via the medical literature in young males' suicide and attempted suicide . Significant interest has emerged too in women who self-harm, particularly through the work of local women's mental health organisations, abuse survivor projects and women in special hospitals. (See for example Arnold, 1995; Threshold Newsletter (1995); Liebling and Chipchase.)

Thus a National Self-harm Network developed through an organisation of psychiatric survivors, Survivors Speak Out, has been gathering momentum during the period of this research. This is a campaigning body which is lobbying for the rights of individuals who self-harm within psychiatry, therapy, accident and emergency departments and so on. (See Pembroke, 1994.) Though to some extent self-harm has in the past been viewed as a 'women's issue', awareness of the plight of young men who self-harm has grown — for example through the study of attempted suicide and self-harm in male prisons (Liebling and Karup, 1993).

It might be wondered whether a tendency could develop both for those who attempt suicide and for those who self-harm to see themselves as being treated worse. This in turn could lead to the possibility of rivalry between those concentrating on self-harm and those concentrating on suicide, for example in research funding, service provision and service users' views. Thus the recent, positive developments in understanding self-harm may implicitly assume that individuals who attempt suicide are in some ways 'treated better' and that their situation is better researched than that of self-harmers. Alternatively research into attempted suicide which suggests that self-harm is primarily 'malingering' and a 'suicidal gesture' may in turn be failing to recognise the specific functions and meanings of this behaviour for those who harm themselves.

Research methods

As has already been emphasised, this research project sought to avoid such over-simplifications. In order to begin to understand the more complex meanings of the young people's behaviour and the emotions it generated, it was essential that its methods enabled it to penetrate the ways in which they made sense of attempted suicide and self-harm. A further aim was then to use this articulation of the potential issues and dilemmas they had identified to examine current attempts at intervention and treatment. Clearly, since such aims could not be achieved by questioning young people who had no direct experience of such behaviour, the active participation of those who did have this experience was essential. A key methodological requirement therefore was to make the study as empowering as possible for the young people — for example by viewing them as unique informants on the subject and by developing the research process in ways which gave them considerable ownership of it.

Recruiting the interviewees

The ten in-depth interviews carried out with individual young people each lasted between two and two and a half hours. No strict sampling or standardised recruitment procedures were used. All young people who had used 42nd Street in the previous two years, including current users, were invited to consider participating in the research by, initially, coming to an open meeting. At this, attended by six young people, a guest speaker (a survivor of self-harm) spoke from her own experience and a discussion took place on the possible aims of the research. A range of relevant agencies were also informed of the proposed work and specific projects working with young people on mental health issues were visited in order to invite suggestions and, it was hoped, generate interest in the research.

All the young people who expressed an interest were offered a chance to meet the researcher individually to discuss how they might want to contribute and what the interviews would involve. They were also invited to offer written and other creative material for inclusion in the research and to take part in group discussions. In the event, nine of the young people who participated were contacted through 42nd Street with four becoming involved through other local agencies, and two via 42nd Street users already involved in the research. Of the ten who were interviewed individually, four identified as gay or lesbian.

Though it was seen as important from the start to explore the experiences of both black and white young people, those who actually participated in the research were all white. A great deal of time was spent visiting a variety of projects in Manchester in an attempt, through their workers, to contact black young people. However, discussions with black agencies and black workers showed that, for several reasons, this would not be easy.

Some black workers acknowledged that they did not meet many African-Caribbean young people who had repeatedly attempted suicide or self-harmed and suggested that research involving these young people would need to have a much broader scope aimed at exploring experiences of self-harm within black communities more generally. Though the situation of Asian young people was different, with high rates of self-harm among Asian young women being reported, the Asian workers contacted emphasised how difficult and potentially threatening it would be for Asian young people to talk about their experiences to somebody whom they did not know. For black young people's participation in the research, these contacts with outside agencies also demonstrated the limitations of having a white person carrying out the research.

The individual interviews

The one-to-one interview situation adopted within the research was unfamiliar to the young people who participated. Because to a large extent it was 'contrived', no clear model for it was available from their previous experience to 'guide' them (or indeed the researcher). It was not for example a counselling or a mental health assessment session; but nor was it simply a chat with a friend. Here in fact was a specific example of the participative research process at work, with the 'rules' for the interview, and the relevance and appropriateness of the questions in certain respects being developed and realised during the interviews themselves.

As a result, the one-to-one sessions were not rigidly 'controlled' or standardised: rather they were a variant of the 'semi-structured' interview. A number of questions were devised in advance based on a list of general topic areas about repeated attempted suicide and self-harm. Following some introductory questions, these concentrated on, for example, the difference between attempted suicide and self-harm; the development of 'repetition'; underlying factors; reactions/responses by the services used by the young people; and the benefits for them of attempted suicide and self-harm. This list of questions is included as an appendix.

However, these questions were designed only as a guide. On occasions it did seem appropriate for the researcher/interviewer to offer certain ideas and suggestions to facilitate the interview. However the particular issues which the young person picked out as needing attention during the interview were also explored in depth and detail, including ones which initially had not been anticipated. What was seen to be crucial was that a mutually acceptable way was found for the young person to comment on and voice their views and experience.

It was envisaged from the outset that the researcher's questions might get sidelined so that the interview became more of a free flowing conversation. This was what in effect usually happened, with most of the interview time being spent working through the first question. With this as their prompt, the young people would guide the researcher through their thoughts on their behaviour, on their own personal path towards an understanding of it and on their reactions to it, with the researcher questioning and probing as the process proceeded.

It was assumed initially that one of the reasons why interview questions were necessary was to ensure that discussion did not 'stray off the point'. This however did not happen. Every young person interviewed was eager to discuss their own views of self-harm and what it meant for them. Though they were especially keen to talk about self-harm without suicidal intent, particularly cutting, many of them were also willing to discuss their experiences of overdosing.

Aims of the group discussions

The group discussions were seen as a way of bringing together some young people with recent and current experience of suicide and self-harm with, at the outset, the following aims:

- To add to the stock of knowledge and material developed through the individual interviews — for example, to generate new ideas and insights in a group setting which it may not have been possible for the young people to express through individual contact alone.

- To develop ideas on possible differences and similarities between the perspectives of different young people who 'repeatedly' attempt suicide/self-harm.
- To look at possible changes or 'solutions' to issues young people identified as problematic.
- To try to develop a more 'collective' response amongst the young people to issues related to attempted suicide and self-harm — for example, to the reactions of others, to forms of treatment and the definitions and meanings of the behaviour.

Recruitment to the group meetings

Once the interviews began to take place it became very clear how different and varied the young people's experiences were. Whilst we knew it would be difficult to make any broad generalisations from the research, we did want to provide more than a set of individual accounts. The groups were designed as part of the process of developing a more 'collective' sense of the issues. Also, because the issue seemed to be surrounded by taboo and silence, it was felt that it may be useful to bring people together, thus enabling them to generate and develop ideas through each other. Many of the young people who were interviewed were keen to follow up some of the debate on the issues that had arisen during the interviews and thus it was felt important to develop this understanding through meeting as a small group.

All the young people who had attended the open meeting, or met the researcher to discuss the study, or had been interviewed, were invited to come to the group sessions. Thus, these were not open meetings: everyone who took part in them had had some previous discussion and clarification of the purposes of the research and their involvement in it. This was seen as very important, to ensure that the young people were clear that it was not a support group but a forum in which they could air their views with other young people who had had similar experiences.

In the event a total of ten young people participated in the group sessions, including five who had previously been interviewed. Three of the sessions were each attended by four young people while the fourth had an attendance of two.

The research process in action

As has already been indicated, the research was explicitly designed as an attempt to break out of certain more conventional models of research with a view to beginning to capture the young people's own accounts and perspectives. In order for this to have a chance of happening, many preconceived ideas, explanations and understandings of the issues had therefore as far as possible to be relinquished. Even so, the researcher was unprepared for how far the young people seized the opportunity provided by the research to state their own case and in doing so to push and challenge her. Throughout the research process in fact it became clear that, despite the 'alternative' participatory model being adopted, many of the conventional wisdoms about research and the basic assumptions and approaches which flow from these had not after all been shaken off by the researcher.

The long, carefully prepared questions came to feel increasingly irrelevant for gaining the kinds of insights and material required. In some ways they even came to block the young people's freedom to offer their own agenda and perceptions since these could not be narrowly compartmentalised into the neat sections which the prepared questions imposed. These questions often proved quite inadequate in allowing the young people to represent themselves or to position themselves in relation to their content and meaning.

As the interviews progressed, the young people's own descriptions and insights came increasingly to 'develop' the questions and the dialogue which ensued. As already indicated, their descriptions and understandings required the research to examine areas which had not initially been considered. In fact, to have stayed too rigidly with the original format of questions would have acted as a barrier to many of the most valuable insights and some of the more complex descriptions which the young people offered. The list of questions was thus effectively abandoned as the primary focus of the interviews. Instead — and regardless of how naive the questions might have come to seem at that stage — a check was made at the end of each interview to ensure that they had been covered and that particularly important issues had been discussed.

Once they had been freed from concentrating on helping the young person — and with preconceived notions of what attempted suicide and self-harm might mean for the young person as far as is possible suspended — the interviews became genuine information gathering exercises. Their main functions came to be to explore and discuss, rather than to comment on, what the young person was saying about their behaviour. This in turn facilitated in-depth accounts of this behaviour which in very important ways went beyond many of the initial preconceptions of it which had informed the questions.

In particular the accounts which the young people volunteered moved away from many of the veiled 'why' questions. This has again meant that the study has less to say about particular links which may or may not exist for a young person between their past or present experiences and their attempted suicide and self-harm — that it is less focussed on causes. Instead, as it in fact set out to do, it gives more probing attention to the 'how' questions — to the young people's own descriptions, understanding and meanings of their behaviour. (See Ross and McKay, 1979.)

As a result, the young people who were interviewed offered enormous depth of understanding of their suicide attempts and self-harm, though in relation much more to what it gives them rather than to its causes. At the same time, some of the young people did recognise some history to their behaviour and its links for example with certain events. The important factors the young people identified here included sexual and/or physical abuse, mostly in childhood but also as a young person; bullying; being an outsider and being seen as 'different'; bad reactions to expressions of gay or lesbian sexuality and difficulties in coming out; and the suppression of negative emotions such as anger. Though some of the young people often saw these links clearly, especially in relation to sexual and physical abuse, they still usually concluded that making simple connections between their present behaviour and their past experience was inadequate — that their self-harm meant a great deal more than that.

The process which was set in motion in the individual interviews was continued in the discussion groups. Indeed, their structure was even looser since they were specifically designed to allow the young people to begin to formulate more collective accounts of their experiences and some shared interpretations of them. Here again it soon became clear how far the research approach had failed to free itself from some of the traditional assumptions about what such research should be attempting, how it should be carried out and what the young people might want to do with it.

It also quickly became clear how unfounded were any fears which persisted that, for example, the subject might be too traumatic for the young people to deal with in a group; or that group experience might harm them and 'make them worse'; or that they might stray off the subject matter. In fact, here too, the researcher and a co-facilitator, in a number of ways turned out to be unprepared for the seriousness of the young people's challenge to their approach.

Though the intention had always been to have as open a forum as possible, some form of agenda for the group meetings again seemed important. This was seen as necessary partly to provide some security in this relatively unknown arena but also to ensure that the wider research agenda was covered. Planning for the first group session involved the facilitation of a discussion which would enable the group members to define self-harm and attempted suicide for themselves. A group definition of the issues seemed like a good participative way of starting the work.

However, once again such plans proved to be an obstacle which was effectively overwhelmed by the young people's responses at the very first meeting. For them, this facilitation seemed 'just like psychiatry' in its apparent aim of categorising and labelling them — though now with the additional (and ironic) twist, it seemed, of trying to get them to do this for the researcher! The limitations of what was intended to be a participative and alternative model were thus again revealed, not least because of the extent to which it remained trapped in efforts to simplify and generalise what were very complex and varied experiences: 'the simpler we try and make it, the easier it is to misinterpret'.

Another outcome of the research process was the slight shift in focus from the original 'attempted suicide and self-harm' to one that in the end gave more of an emphasis to self-harm and overdosing (as a form of self-harm). This shift came from the young people themselves: while they engaged in the debate about the relationship between suicide and self-harm, and did talk specifically about suicide, in the end much of the interview and group discussion centred on self-harm. This emphasis is reflected in the report, where the term 'self-harm' is used to cover the different behaviours talked about, including overdosing as self-harm without suicidal intent. Where attempted suicide is specifically being discussed, this is made clear.

The terminology used in this report was chosen with care. Self-harm and attempted suicide were terms that the young people felt comfortable with in talking about their experiences, and it was seen as important to stick to them. The terms 'parasuicide' and 'deliberate self-harm' which are more widely used particularly in medical approaches were avoided. They were not found useful in representing the young people's experiences since in themselves they convey certain interpretations of self-harming behaviour.

What was also made plain by the young people was how important it is to avoid two common attitudes — one that views all suicidal behaviour as a form of self-harm by denying suicide intent, and the other that assumes that all self-harm is always linked to suicidal feelings or actions.

For the aims of the research to have any chance of being achieved — that is, for the expression of the young people's views and opinions to be facilitated — it was thus impossible merely to persist with the original carefully planned agendas. Some positive response had to be made to the challenges which the young people were posing.

This did not mean that the young people took over control of the research process: indeed, as they themselves pointed out in the group meetings, the research would be *'your (the researcher's) interpretation of things said'*. However, it did mean that, as understood by researchers, 'findings' in a conventional sense would be difficult to discover and write up. This was likely to be particularly true if (as was the whole idea of the project!) the research were to take what the young people were saying seriously. Great care also had be taken not to impose too many assumptions about the nature of the behaviour itself, its meanings or what caused it. And it meant not generalising too broadly about it or oversimplifying the issues arising from it.

By its very nature, the research was thus never going to provide easy or unambiguous answers or 'solutions' to the issues with which it was dealing. However, the open-ended and responsive research 'medium' which was adopted, by striving positively to affirm the young people and validate their perspectives, would seem in itself to have conveyed to them some powerful if implicit messages about the aims of the research and their central role in achieving these. That is, the very processes it set in motion did seem to encourage and validate some articulation of the views — including ones on the development of support services — of a normally marginalised and ignored group of young people. The research aims, at the very least, included increasing awareness of and fuelling debate on the complexity of the issues involved; clarifying the depth and variety of the individual experiences of these; highlighting the dilemmas faced by the young people and their workers; and beginning to dispel many of the myths and stereotypes about the young people themselves.

As a result, the accounts which these young people gave of their experience, its variety and its complexity were both powerful and lucid. They provided valuable insights into the importance and the many functions and meanings of their behaviour in their lives, including its potential risks and problems. They offered important comments on and criticisms of existing services and responses. And they injected ideas on the development of more accepting and open support strategies and crisis facilities. Whatever criticisms may be levelled at the research methodology of this project, the authenticity of these 'findings' would seem to be very difficult to deny or contradict.

Textual Note

Readers are urged not to give way to a temptation to 'skip' the quotations included throughout the report on the implicit assumption that the text is 'what it's really about'. The quotations are taken from what the young people said and so are the very foundation of the research.

Chapter 1 ('A Few Hours Break') for example, which sets out the young people's descriptions of the 'functions' of their suicide attempts and their self-harming, is made up almost entirely of quotations from the individual interviews. As such it is crucial to understanding the remaining chapters of the report. Unless those involved in this area of work begin to comprehend what the young person's behaviour gives to them, then their knowledge about what is appropriate and needed, and the interventions they adopt, are bound to be deeply flawed. Only when the young people were given space to articulate some of their thoughts and experiences within an emotional and social context which they defined did the complexity of their behaviour start to become intelligible .

All uncredited quotations in italics are from the young people. All but two of the chapter titles are taken from the young people's own words because they seemed to highlight the key issues to be explored in that chapter. The exceptions are 'My Own Special Creation' and 'Who's Hurting Who?' both of which are explicit interpretations of what the young people said.

It was quiet,
The room was quiet, everything was.

She switched on her music,
the volume was all consuming.
The paper-thin blade laughed,
As her arm, silent, lay down.

Then to its job.
Noise was released,
Great shouting and fighting
and choking and crying
and pleading and begging
and anger and hate
screamed down her arm.

They all laughed
As they dripped off her hand,
free to play and shout
and laugh and fight-
Bright colours, and warm.

The mouths on her arm
were still screaming
and crying and screaming.
She tried to shut them up
with a towel.
But they bit into her
and still they screamed
and would not let go of her,
their lips curled back to show
bared teeth, snarling.

By day she muffled their cries
with a sleeve,
'til their scared lips
sealed silent shut.

CHAPTER 1

'A Few Hours Break'

Young people's accounts of the 'functions' of their behaviour

The explanations often attributed to self-harm and attempted suicide by those who do not self-harm prominently include, for example, that they are forms of manipulation or of attention-seeking. The research undertaken for this study suggests that such explanations are inadequate.

Indeed, the young people interviewed for this study tended to see self-harm and attempted suicide more as intrapersonal than interpersonal acts — that is, as having more to do with what it does for them than with the effects their behaviour has, or might have, on other people.

This chapter will therefore focus on what these young people said about the 'functions' as they saw them of their attempts to harm themselves. Far from starting by seeing such suicidal and self-injurious behaviour as nonsensical or pathological, it seeks to present young people's rationale for this and how they described what it accomplished for them. After considering the 'benefits' it brought them, the focus will move to possible functions for communicating with others — though hopefully the difficulty of making clear distinctions between these two perspectives will also become apparent.

As in Arnold's recent study of women who self-harm, the young people in our study offered enormous insights into their motives for their self-harm and gave answers of "great variety, depth and subtlety" (1995: 16). Indeed, it is not easy to distinguish and separate out the various functions which self-harm may have for a young person. They may be interrelated; they may suggest many different simultaneous purposes; they may be used differently by the same person at different times. The self-harm may thus have multiple meanings for the same individual. Two young woman in our study talking about self-harm — cutting in particular — summed this up:

> *You can use it just as anything: a multi-purpose coping mechanism!*

> *I just think it's just different ways of coping at different times with different things.*

The young people offered a variety of reasons for the harm they inflicted on themselves. These reasons were more to do with what it did for them at the time they were doing it than, in any direct sense, because of something which had happened to them in the past. Certainly essential links between their past and the self-harm were recognised. However, for them, the reasons for harming themselves were more about the immediate gains which they felt they could get from the act.

> *I just know how it makes me feel. I don't have like a 100% knowledge about why I do it because part of me just doesn't know. I can only figure out what I think it could be.*

Some of the functions of self-harm identified by the young people in the study included:

- getting rid of unwanted and distressing feelings and emotions;
- not having to think about painful (and preoccupying) memories, thoughts or worries;
- getting out of a difficult situation for a while;
- providing relief from and release of distress;
- creating a situation of comfort and security, like a 'haven in a heartless world'; and
- focussing or transferring emotional pain onto a physical, more manageable and tangible 'thing'.

Extensive quotations from what the young people themselves said will be used to illustrate and clarify these various functions. The headings are rather artificial as many of the functions are interlinked and overlap. However they are adopted in an attempt to break down the functions and help to draw out possible distinctions.

A RANGE OF FUNCTIONS

A few hours break

> *When I cut myself, things which are overwhelming you in your daily life aren't, just for five minutes, maybe an hour or however long I think about cutting myself and doing it and all the after care. All of that becomes paramount, and everything else, like big situations, exams, boyfriends, the bastard that can't go to prison, becomes far less important — I don't even think about it usually, until afterwards. It used to give me a few hours break and quite often I'd do it and sometimes fall asleep afterwards because I was just so worn out and that was great because I'd have a wonderful sleep and I'd be able to sleep which is something I'd find really difficult.*

A release mechanism: releasing/relieving pressure

It's like a release mechanism . . . it is for me and it works and no psychiatrist can disagree with me because it does work but they've never known what to say to you because they're all in their little worlds, like 'no you shouldn't do this' and 'it could be fatal'. But if you know what you're doing then it's not fatal if you don't want it to be . . . do you know what I mean? Because you know about how deep your veins and fat cells are underneath your skin.

It's like a release. It feels better after I've taken tablets and I feel better after I've cut myself to pieces.

Release of anger

(When I had attempted suicide by crashing my car) I think it got it out of my system, I suppose. To be honest I don't think what I felt when I was doing the car was all of it, it was just half of it. It wasn't all of my anger, just some of it. I think it helped because I only had to deal with half the anger then.

Putting the situation on hold

I wanted to be doing it all the time but felt I had to put on a bit of a normality show for everyone else, so a compromise. So I wouldn't really look after myself — there wasn't the time. Perhaps it was because if I didn't look after it then it would be kind of like just continuous ongoing thing because that's really what I wanted. A way of putting the situation 'on hold' . . . I suppose in a way it got me through the exams because it was a way of not thinking about stuff what's happened, the situation, because the more I cut the less I think about it — that's definitely true and I didn't want to think about it at all . . . After a few months, once I wasn't thinking about it much anyway, I wasn't needing to think about it so much anyway so I didn't need to cut as much to stop me thinking about it.

An exit strategy

I needed to know that I could get out of a situation if I needed to . . . to know that I could if I needed to.

(When I was cutting myself I was) thinking of perhaps killing myself. I thought if I can get away from this it'll help . . . so I did it again.

To get out of it for a while

I just wanted to be warm and blank, to go to sleep and stay there.

I just wanted to go to sleep until things were different. I don't know until when or whatever.

Not suicide as such, but like taking too many tablets, overdosing to relieve pressure like wanting out, but not necessarily wanting to kill myself . . . I was in the flat on my own, I took an overdose to see how many I could take to knock me out, and then I'd wake up again the next day.

To prevent worse happening

I started cutting . . . I found it ok so I did it more. But I was careful. It wasn't suicide, more the opposite. It was more like wanting to stop it ending up in suicide. To keep you in check, to keep you going.

It's like a mad feeling in your stomach, it's like pressure all building up and if you don't release it out, you would, I don't know, blow up.

A haven: not having to think/worry about things

Cutting myself kind of creates a haven. I don't think about what else has gone on.

I want my attention to be away from the situation — especially when I don't know what to do — I get really confused and panicky and I didn't know what to do.

Just a pain instead of like actual feelings, or if something's getting on your case I find that cutting can like preoccupy you as well. It would give me something else in me head.

When my boyfriend is going away, I get upset — but then I'd do it and it wouldn't really matter because it's like fuck it, I could be dead soon. It's like everything's lifted. You don't have to worry about it anymore because you could be dead soon. It's like a really great sense of relief. It's like everything's gone, it's great.

A distraction: to preoccupy or focus your mind

Cutting yourself is like a distraction . . . to remove you, dislodge you from where you are and what you're feeling.

At first it was about taking it out on myself — the feelings, blaming myself and to distract my mind from what it was I was feeling and thinking. To make it into something physical, to take your mind off it for a while. It's a way of focussing it.

Thinking about it or doing something about it was more painful than actually doing it (harming myself). Doing it is painful but not really painful. (Thinking about it) was the worst thing. That's more painful . . . so that's why I'd do it again because it was less painful than thinking about it . . . because it's something which goes into your whole life. When you've got a thought going on in your head and you just can't forget about it, something painful, thinking about it would open up a *big can of things. It would go around your head for ages and you just can't think about anything else or do anything, because all the time you're looking at the world and you're thinking about it all the time — I think that's <u>more painful</u>, even though it's more positive and all those things — it's <u>loads</u> more painful because you can't control anything about it except by totally not thinking about it. The only thing you can do if you can't do anything about it is to totally not think about it . . . Cutting means that you can think about something completely different — you can think about that.*

To counteract the emotional pain

I think the physical has a lot to do with it — taking the pain away from what's in your head and transferring it onto your body.

(Usually it doesn't hurt) but I remember once I felt it hurt, but the physical pain sort of took over the emotional hurt, so I suppose it sort of counteracted it out.

To replace saying things

With the cutting, sometimes like when I'm feeling totally 'off it', I just don't know what to say. I find it easier just to cut up.

To clear my mind

If you're feeling really, say, down and got no energy and if you cut yourself you're getting a pain there — it just tends to relieve it and take it away for a bit . . . and clear my mind . . . more focussed . . . and then you're not thinking about perhaps doing yourself in anymore. It's like taking yourself out of a cluttered room and into a nice room with nice clean walls. It's hard to describe but it's like a relief.

So nothing can harm you

(Self-harm, cutting and overdosing) takes you out of the world around you. It makes you more introverted so nothing can bother you, harm you — psychologically anyway.

Security/safety

I carry round with me blades and stuff sometimes in case things get really bad. I prefer to do it at home and cope with it. (It's) a bit like a safety blanket. I suppose I feel better with it because I know if I need to I can go and do it if someone's on your back.

To feel things

— that is, for example, to feel different, special, worthwhile, a sense of achievement, pride, personal endurance. (See Chapter 4: 'My Own Special Creation'.)

> *It was everything, like a wave of what I was feeling.*

Taking things out on myself

— self punishment, to express annoyance with self, to change the way you are, to make yourself do something you don't want to do. (See Chapter 5: 'A Bad Apple'.)

To forget things . . .

> *I put the scars to the back of my mind and think that I haven't done any — you don't have to remember them and so then you don't have to remember all the stuff that was going on.*

. . . and to remember things

> *Every scar has its own like photograph book that makes you remember stuff because I don't seem to forget about which ones I did.*

Throwing away all the badness

> *It's like absolute power. Seeing the blood coming out — mopping it up with tissues and throwing it away is like throwing away all the badness.*

FUNCTIONS LINKED TO SEXUAL ABUSE

Though, as will be argued later, the connections are far from straightforward (see Chapter 3: 'A Clock Ticking'), the comment of one young woman seemed to capture the link between attempted suicide and self-harm and sexual abuse.

> *It's got to come out.*

Young male and young female survivors of sexual abuse often talked of specific functions linked to their abuse, including releasing badness and pressure. This link, particularly between cutting and abuse, has been acknowledged previously in various ways, with some writers suggesting a possible connection with healing for the person doing it (for example Favazza and Favazza, 1987).

To cleanse me

> *I just sit and hold my head and think, I've got to get rid of it — I'll take some tablets — annadins, four or five — then four or five paracetamol — hour later see*

what happens — oh no it's not going, tried that, the only thing left. If I only cut just the once and see the blood coming out of my veins then it'll cleanse me — make me feel that I've released all this dirt that's sticking to my veins — and I would — I'd cut once and I'd immediately feel the pressure released. Dirt, grit coming out. It would feel 'gritty' — scraping against the skin as it came out — I go quite deep — sometimes to the bone.

Releasing the pressure in my head

What made me think of it? I don't know. Just frustration really. I was trying to eat my dinner, I was sat on my own. I couldn't see, I looked around, thought I was going blind. I was going mad, I couldn't stand the pain. I stabbed the food and then all of a sudden I turned and stabbed my arm. It didn't break the skin and I kept going and going until it went through the skin and I pulled it out and all this blood started trickling down my arm and I just watched it and it felt like it was releasing the pressure in my head, like releasing all the bad blood and maggots. I knew it wasn't (maggots and stuff) but it was to me.

It's like I could feel my arms kind of tingling and itching — and it was like, Oh God it's the dirt in the blood and it's piling up and it's going to cause blood clots so get it out. So I would cut once and then cut even deeper and to me it looked like sand and dirt. After being raped and things you feel like gunk and stuff is stuck to your insides and seeping into your veins and it's making me bad because they're bad for doing this because I knew it was wrong. Their badness is getting in to me so I've got to let it out. I've got to let this badness out otherwise it's going to start eating me from the inside and it's going to crawl out of my skin.

To release bad situations/experiences

(I'd do it) just to feel better, to make the wound bigger — to make the wound big enough so stuff would come out because I used to visualise that the blood was either people or situations or stuff like that and it was _that_ was coming out and not blood. And I was convinced for ages that I wasn't doing self-harm and that it wasn't blood but it just looked like that because it had to find a way out, and that's the only way it could find a way out . . . It was those bits that I could imagine coming out. It might seem really weird but I could actually see places and people coming out of me and it wasn't like it was blood, it didn't look anything like blood . . . (it was more) like a postcard or a clay model coming out of me . . . I'd never tell the psychiatrist that's what I saw — I just say it's about escape. I never told him the whole thing because I'm always scared that if I do then they'll see me as psychotic and all that.

To get back at abuser(s)

> *I started to cut my arms. I felt like I deserved it. It felt like it wasn't towards myself, it was towards them (my abusers) — the way I coped. I get relief from it in certain situations.*

> *I'm going to hurt myself so much that I'll end up hurting the people who say that they love me.*

> *(Overdosing) — Because I was abused I thought they were inside my body, my body felt filthy and disgusting . . . so it felt like I was hurting them, even though in real terms I was obviously hurting myself and damaging my insides, but it didn't feel that way, it felt like I was getting into them . . . I felt like I was cleaning it out because I had a lot of filth inside me and that (overdosing) clears it away . . . the abuser's been inside me so that's why it feels like it's not all me, there's a bit of them there and it feels disgusting and I have to get to it and that's how it's always been.*

These feelings of badness and anger are explored in more detail in Chapter 5: A Bad Apple.

SPECIFIC FUNCTIONS CONCERNED WITH CONTROL

> *I think control's a big thing, when you can't control what's happening around you . . . you can't control pressure from outside, from society but you can to yourself.*

> *Controlling, something for once in your life — it's a good feeling.*

> *(It's about) keeping control. Taking it out on yourself. You have no control over what people think about you, what they say . . . You've got to have control over something . . . self-harm . . . so you take it out on yourself.*

> *The only way is to try and take yourself to the limit so you're in control of yourself and your environment.*

> *(It's) difficult to explain what it's like when I'm doing it. I feel very much in control, absolutely in control.*

> *Although people think self-harm is about being out of control it's something very <u>in control</u> that you do because it <u>puts you</u> in control, when you're doing it you're in control of yourself. So then to take it all away from you, I think that's why you want to do it again, it's because everything you've just spent hours building up has just been taken away from you.*

That control may be a crucial thread running through many of the functions of self-harm is in line with other recent material written on women and self-harm.

> "Control is a meaning that I have found to be absolutely invariable and the most fundamental."   (Burstow, 1992: 195)

"For some women self-harm provided an important sense of control. Where a woman felt powerless, hurting herself helped her feel that she could exercise some control, even if only over the injuries, pain, bleeding and scarring of her own body. Some women also felt that by injuring themselves they controlled their feelings of anger and their possibilities of their hurting someone else." (Arnold, 1995: 15)

The many meanings of control

Control in this context may be multi-faceted. It may, for example, mean wanting to keep yourself under control; or being able to do something which other people cannot control; or harming yourself in order to lose control and then come back as a way of getting back into control.

You can do loads with cutting — you can lose control, be spontaneous, lose your temper... cutting was good because you could do it all over the place and you can really freak out.

The young people also recognised the contradictory and unstable nature of this control so that, when the self-harm developed into a need to do it, it lost its control element. The control then could seemingly come from not doing it — though not doing it would fail to fulfil many of the functions allotted to it. Considerable confusion could thus exist about such control.

To me it feels awful because it's about control and yet is it control when I cut up or when I don't cut up?

Young people could also lose the control when other people tried to 'get in on it' — for example, by trying to take it away or regulating it, or even perhaps by just getting to know about it and/or talking about it.

Confusing the issues

As we can see, various forms of self-harm mean and express much more for the young person than a 'suicidal gesture', a failed suicide attempt, attention-seeking. Just as self-harm by 'cutting up' has often been confused with a failed suicide attempt, so too in some cases has overdosing. In fact, this could be used by the young person to get out of a difficult and painful situation or when for a while they were feeling agitated, frustrated, out of control, overwhelmed by thoughts and feelings.

When I've overdosed — just to get out of it, I've usually told somebody that I've taken too many tablets. People don't understand that. They think that if you've taken an overdose then you want to kill yourself but sometimes it's not. In my case it's not.

This confusion in other people about what self-harm or attempted suicide involves may be an outcome of their best intentions — such as their concern for the young person's life or safety. However it may have the effect of breaking trust, or of making the young person feel controlled and judged, misunderstood and even punished. This in turn can feed into the spiral of feeling alone-bad-wrong-controlled.

Coping

Overdosing, cutting and other forms of self-harm could therefore, at some points in a young person's life, offer them immediate benefits — for example, by bringing relief from difficult and often unbearable situations and from emotional distress.

To some people this way of coping may seem rather odd or extreme. It may however not be all that unusual. We know that people cope with stress in their own way: to avoid dealing with personal pressures or painful experiences such as bereavement, abuse, relationship difficulties or loneliness: they may for example overwork or drink heavily. Self-harm may have similar functions.

Some people at some time may have 'tried it' (harmed themselves) without it doing much for them — that is without their getting any feeling of relief or benefit. However, when their situation changed, when they were experiencing extreme distress, when they were unable to cope, it could be used or recalled. Sometimes it could have a different effect in different immediate situations or under different circumstances.

One young woman for example, recalling how as a teenager she cut her wrists while thinking of suicide, acknowledged that it really hurt. Then she did it only a couple of times.

> *I didn't really know how to cope but I had the feeling that this wasn't the way.*

A few years later, in the midst of an abusive, violent relationship, the self-harm took on a new meaning and began to give her something.

> *(When) I really started doing it, it was completely different that time — yes I had exams but I wasn't that bothered. I was in a violent relationship and had been attacked by this guy who'd been an absolute bastard to me and I didn't know what the hell was going on. I was hearing voices in my head and I thought I was going completely insane. I think looking back I probably was, but I didn't, just sheer luck. All hell broke loose. I was drinking like a fish, I was smoking loads, nothing was going right and I just started cutting myself. I can't even remember why I did it the first time, I think it was because I'd looked back and remembered doing it last time. I was so distressed and I thought, well I'll try it again and I absolutely loved it and I just carried on doing it and did it April, May, June, July, August, September.*

CHAPTER 2

'The Next Best Thing'

The relationship between suicide and self-harm: problems and risks

An important but complex relationship appears to exist between suicide and self-harm. As we have already seen, it is dangerously inadequate to portray self-harm as a suicidal gesture or as a failed suicide attempt. This misses the point of the specific functions which self-harm may have for a young person. Indeed at some points attempted suicide may be a survival strategy which even helps to avert suicide.

At the same time it is also inadequate to view self-harm as always concerned with coping and survival. This section will look at this relationship in more detail and examine some of the problems and risks associated with repeated self-harm.

Self-harm as the next best thing to suicide

For many of the young people interviewed, self-harm began while thinking about suicide. In desperate situations which were pushing them into thinking about ways out, even of attempting suicide and seeking death, self-harm could act as *'the next best thing'*.

> *I'd been in a situation I wasn't happy with and I didn't know what to do and I was really miserable and fed up and wanted to be dead and I thought I'm not going to kill myself so what's the next best thing so I can just get out of this situation for a few hours.*

> *It's like wanting to be dead but not wanting to kill yourself. I'd think about taking an overdose or jumping off a bridge, but I'd think 'No, I'll do this instead'. It's very blurred.*

> *First time I cut myself I was thinking about suicide — then it carried on. Got the idea from that. I needed to know that I could get out of a situation if I needed to.*

Self-harm as the opposite to suicide

The above represents a link between suicide and self-harm which may mean that the one (self-harm) acts to prevent the other (suicide). This has been recognised in some of the literature on self-harm which sees self-harm as, in some respects, a positive coping strategy. Maris (1971) argued that women who repeatedly attempt suicide or self-harm should be seen as using 'life preserving defences' through engaging in partial self-destruction aimed at making life possible rather than at ending it. More recently Favazza and Favazza (1987) have talked about suicide being averted when the person concerned makes a form of sacrifice which substitutes the 'destruction of body part for the destruction of the whole body.'

> Started cutting with razor blades — small cuts. Found it ok so I did it more, but I was careful, not suicidal — the opposite. More like wanting to stop it ending up in suicide. To keep you in check, to keep you going.

> So I wanted to kill myself but I didn't. What I'd do is cut first and see if that made me feel any better.

Some young people drew a clear distinction between self-harm and suicide.

> For me, it's not about life or death or anything like that, it's just a way of coping.

> I attempted suicide when I felt things had badly gone wrong. It's when I can't see any chance of things changing . . . self-harm is a more optimistic approach, a way out.

Whilst much of the time self-harm acted as a form of survival, at the same time there was some recognition, not so much that self-harm leads to suicide, but that sometimes the feelings underlying much of it could get so bad that the distinction could blur.

> I don't cut myself to kill myself, but at times it can get like that.

> If I was thinking about suicide I would start cutting up first to see how that made me feel and if that wasn't enough then I would, yes — I would attempt it. But I've never had to do that. When I've attempted suicide I've always meant it and when I've cut up I've always meant to just cut up.

An inherent vicious circle?

For many of the young people an inherent vicious circle to their self-harm seemed to exist. This could manifest itself in various ways.

For one thing, self-harm could in some respects become 'addictive', partly because of the multi-purpose functions it served. It thus could develop into a need to do it. When this happened it could to some extent lose some of its most important functions (for example, to do with control). At that point the self-harm could become somewhat confused with being an end in itself like addictions, instead of helping to achieve other limited aims and serving particular functions.

I'm addicted to it because I've been on it most of my life.

I think it's infectious when you cut up because it makes you feel so much better afterwards that you do it over and over again to get that feeling again. It's infectious in that way anyway.

I don't think there is a cure for cutting up. I think once you've done it you're more likely to do it again.

Compulsion. I hadn't done it for a while so I thought I'd have to do it to get some relief . . . cutting is an addiction now — something that needs doing to get relief. You feel happy after.

Though for a time the self-harm could serve these functions and act as a coping or survival strategy, ultimately it could not solve the underlying issues with which it was attempting to deal. Presumably the young person's 'self-administered treatment' could not work. Thus, though able to describe how each time the self-harm seemed to release particular situations — for example, memories of events which had taken place in childhood — one young woman also acknowledged limits to the extent to which it would 'work'.

Q — So each time you can get a particular situation out?

Yes, but the only thing that tends to happen is that the same thing keeps coming out, so you can never actually get rid of it all.

For this young woman, attempting suicide would often become a viable option when she could no longer get the relief or release she felt she needed.

Self-defeating

Despite all its various functions, some young people still felt that their self-harm was self-defeating. Sometimes they were left feeling worse than they had felt before, partly because of guilt, shame and embarrassment at what they had done and partly because it reinforced their feelings of being bad. (See Chapter 5: 'A Bad Apple'.) Afterwards, some of these feelings could be engendered at least in part by negative reactions of others to the behaviour. (See Chapter 6: 'Not A Clue'.)

This sense of relief and security lasts for a while afterwards, until it heals.

(Overdosing) you're oblivious to it and you feel great, and it's that feeling that makes it worthwhile. It just makes you feel good and I don't think people realise that you don't feel good beforehand and you don't feel good afterwards, but when

you're doing it, and for a certain amount of time before you start feeling ill, you do feel good. It's like you don't care, nothing gets to you anymore, you don't give a toss about anything — but then you feel worse than you felt before you took them so it doesn't make sense really.

At the same time, again because of the many functions which the self-harm served, not doing it could make a young person feel worse.

It actually makes me feel worse when I don't do it. Cutting myself stops the pain.

This then represented a sharp dilemma for the young person: doing it may make them feel better in the short term but in some ways worse some time afterwards; while not doing it, by providing no release, could make the feelings build up. This could mean that at times they can't win either way. This perhaps also clarifies why the decision could often fall on the side of doing it rather than not doing it, since at least this guaranteed feeling better for a while, even if only for a very short while.

Increase in severity

As has already been indicated, for many of the young people their self-harm had in some way to increase in severity in order for it to achieve its familiar functions. This could mean that an individual had to take more pills, or cut more and more deeply, to get the same results.

(My) self-harm has got more serious, from little cuts to an armful of scars.

I think you have to do it more and more and do larger cuts to get the same effects.

When self-harm isn't enough

Even when, for most of the time, the young people drew a clear distinction between suicide and self-harm, for some of them self-harm was on occasions not enough. Sometimes, though they had tried harming themselves — for example by cutting up — it had failed to have the effect to which they have become accustomed. In other words, at these moments, it *'doesn't work.'* It then became a case of: *'if hurting myself doesn't make it any better, what will?'* This could lead to a need to go further and increase the harm done. Then, the 'logical' next step could be a suicide attempt.

In such circumstances of desperation, what sometimes became paramount was the need to get out of a situation or state of mind — to stop certain feelings or memories — if the functions of self-harm were still to be served. A young person then may have used whatever means necessary to achieve this — for example, perhaps cutting deeper and deeper, or taking more and more tablets, or mixing cutting and overdosing.

Then I would cut and cut and cut and cut. There'd be too much pressure. So then I wanted to kill myself and I'd take tablets, anything to make me feel better — kill myself — to get away from it all and not have to cope with it anymore.

Sometimes I would cut and it didn't do anything and I would cut again and it didn't do anything and I would cut again and it didn't do anything and then I would cut again and I would feel like I'd lost and I'd think about finishing it. It wasn't easing it, it's not making me feel any better about my life, my situation, myself.

At that point my mind was set on suicide. I seem to have a general pattern (sort of like a pattern) where I cut up a few times (four or five, something like that, sometimes less) and then it sort of makes me feel so much better after doing it, that the only way I can see how to survive is to commit suicide. I know it sounds really stupid to say that, but that's what it feels like.

Here the line between suicide and self-harm could become extremely blurred. Either to 'just self-harm' or to attempt suicide was unlikely to be a calculated or premeditated act. The individual might not know at the outset how much damage they might or might not do to themselves. This could depend for the young person on how much it takes to get a sense of relief from what was going on in their lives: a case of *'anything to make me feel better.'* The result could be a serious threat to their life.

However in these situations deciding whether it was a 'real' suicide attempt might not be straightforward. Though enquiring about suicidal intent could seem crucial, this unfortunately was rarely easy to gauge and, if the point were laboured with the young person, could be a misunderstanding of their situation and therefore be unhelpful .

As we have seen, at times self-harm could represent a valid coping strategy. However, for many young people who repeatedly attempt suicide or self-harm, intense suicidal feelings could be very real to the point where they contradicted the myth that 'they'll never really do it'.

Recently I really wanted to kill myself — it got so bad. It scared me. Before, I'd always been able to decide not to, not to lose control. It was really strong and over-powering.

Last time I went unconscious, when I did my wrists . . . and when I woke up I cried my heart out because I really wanted to be dead.

I had intentions of going (cutting) deeper to the muscle bit. I did want to die, very much, at that point.

It doesn't work anymore

The specific functions which self-harm had for some of these young people might have some kind of an internal limit to their usefulness. For some self-harm generally worked so that it was only occasionally that they felt that they needed to do more. For others, their self-harm no longer, as a whole, worked for them.

> *Self-harm ties in a lot for me with suicide. With self-harm, when there's no release from it — then a suicide attempt. The two, in the last couple of years, have gone hand in hand. Because the self-harm isn't working anymore — it hasn't got the release anymore because I've done it for so long. It doesn't work any more.*

A step closer

The self-harm of some of the young people could represent a 'deep down' desire for suicide and death through a slow process through which they would ultimately control their own fate. Again although this should not be over-generalised, it could for some be an important, even essential, element of their self-harm. It could be more true for young people who overdosed or overdosed and self-harmed repeatedly, rather than for the ones who 'just' self-harm.

> *Because each time you do it you fuck yourself up so it doesn't matter if you don't do it all in one go. You might not do it in one big go but each time you do it you're getting a step closer.*

> *Overdosing — it makes you feel better because you think you're going to drift off into a big long sleep, it dulls your brain and you do think deep down you're going to die.*

> *I don't want to die of a disease — I want to die in my own time, to control it. It's my life and I want to take it away when I want to.*

Self-harm gone wrong

With self-harm a high risk of accidental death could exist, particularly because of the possibility of an increase in the severity of the acts.

> *Some suicide attempts can be self-harm gone wrong — although kind of thinking about death but really self-harm afterwards — for a few minutes wanting to die.*

> *I've several times cut myself with the intention of it being a build up to killing myself and yet it hasn't. But people do accidentally commit suicide.*

> *I don't do these things to die but it scares me because I know one day I'll end up dead . . . I'll do it wrong.*

In addition, repeated self-harm could by its very nature reinforce a young person's feelings of being alone, of their marginalisation, of their sense of being bad. (See Chapter 4: 'My Own Special Creation'; Chapter 5: 'A Bad Apple'.)

The system's abusing me now

This vicious circle could also be perpetuated by treatment interventions which often, to the young person, appeared punitive. These could also fail to recognise the young person's specific needs and could seek to classify their behaviour as <u>either</u> attempted suicide <u>or</u> as parasuicide. As we have seen, such reactions can be unhelpful.

Some specific forms of intervention could actually mean that some young people unwittingly put their lives seriously at risk. These included measures which attempted to prevent the self-harm without dealing with the underlying issues facing a young person. Some young people expressed the sense that *'the longer it builds up the harder it is to relieve it'*. For an individual who felt pressurised into stopping, the effect thus could be that, when they eventually did it, they had to go further to achieve the same feeling.

This could also be the case when, in general, a young person felt controlled. Usually this was felt to be the situation in a hospital setting. One young woman had such fear of being sectioned that, she claimed, if it did ever happen to her again she would *'rather die'*. Many others felt that their experience of hospital had increased their level of·self-harm.

> *My arms are in a state now through being in there, they weren't as bad before, I started taking loads of pills then as well.*

> *I was watched, observed in the ward for four days once and they took everything off me but as soon as I got out I did it again. I got put straight back in again. That wound me up more than anything.*

> *It's like having everything done for you . . . that kind of environment (hospital) makes you react so badly that you just want to do it more — they might give a shit about <u>why</u> but they're not allowed to really. They just patch you up, deal with it. My friend who'd been in hospital after cutting wrists agreed with me — like afterwards you just want to go out and do it again.*

For these young people there was a sense in which some treatment interventions could set the scene for repeated suicide attempts and self-harming which could increase in severity and frequency. As has been argued elsewhere (Pembroke: 1994), being caught up in the medical/psychiatric system can continue the cycle of harm so that this involvement becomes another way in which an individual harms themselves or gets harmed. As one young man put it:

> *The system's abusing me now.*

A complex link thus exists between suicide and self-harm. The young people were often well aware of the potential dangers of their behaviour — indeed, much of the time this was the point.

At the same time, it is important to retain a sense of perspective. Although it is important to recognise the potential risks and problems, we are not arguing that self-harm ultimately leads to suicide. This link might be as strong as, for example, for an individual who smokes, drinks, uses drugs excessively. Overstating the link between self-harm and suicide might to some extent represent a cultural bias against certain forms of coping mechanisms in comparison with others which are more socially acceptable.

The other side to this — self-harm as survival — has been briefly considered and will be looked at in more depth in the next chapter. Indeed, an important conflict needs to be recognised and developed; between, on the one hand, self-harm as increasing self-damage and, on the other, self-harm as a multi-purpose coping mechanism.

CHAPTER 3

'A Clock Ticking'

Young people's descriptions of their self-harm.

I didn't tell anybody. It started off with scalpels. It used to be just a long scratch up my arm. It started off — not very deep. (I was) eleven to twelve years old.

I used to hit myself — I would get mad with myself and hit myself, bit by bit — a bit harder beating me head on the walls. I did it last year, when I was at school.

This chapter highlights the variety of ways the young people described their self-harm. In doing this it emphasises the differences of the experience, both for the individual at different times and between individual young people.

Frequency

Though some young people harmed themselves infrequently as a response to particularly difficult feelings and situations, for many, at certain times in their lives, their self-harm became strikingly frequent.

I did it quite regularly — once or twice a week, then three or four times, then five times a week, then daily...

I used to do it every day, as much as possible.

When it started

A few of the young people identified clearly when their self-harm started.

(The) first time I harmed myself — I was about four — stabbed myself in the arm with a fork, seeing blood — and thinking afterwards, god this feels good... When I was about eight I started using razor blades.

More commonly, many of the young people expressed some confusion and uncertainty on this issue. Sometimes they only realised that their self-harm had begun earlier than they had previously envisaged when they thought about their self-harm in relation to others or when reading some of the recent literature on the subject. (This could perhaps be explained as a young person denying or repressing some of their memories of their self-harm).

Thus, some of the young people recalled banging their head as a young child or eating harmful substances such as glass, and queried: *'does that count?'* The variety of ways for hurting themselves which they had developed at different times in their lives might also partially explain why frequently they were unclear about when the self-harming had started.

> *I can't really remember very clearly when it started.*

> *I keep forgetting bits.*

Some of the young people related the start of their self-harm to the period in their lives when they were experiencing some form of childhood physical and/or sexual abuse and thinking often about how to get away. For others who had identified this link their self-harm seemed to start when they had actually managed to leave the abuse or after it had stopped. Though these young people might have thought about harming themselves and/or attempting suicide before, they had not acted on these feelings. As one young male survivor of childhood physical and sexual abuse recalled:

> *The first time I harmed myself was when I was sixteen and I ran away from home, but I had feelings of suicide when I was living at home but never actually did anything. I cut myself slightly, not very deep or anything. I just couldn't cope. It wasn't like the way I'm doing it now — it was different.*

Some young people reflected that they had begun harming themselves when they had felt controlled. Some dated it to when they had felt that they had lost their childhood, their innocence. For others it seemed to start when they had become more free to express their feelings and emotions — for example, after they had left home and had been released from the routine and structure to which they had been accustomed.

As we have already seen, many of the young people harmed themselves in order to protect themselves from painful feelings and memories. Once they had begun to think about the underlying issues, at least for a short time their self-harm might have started to increase, presumably as a familiar way of dealing with these emotions and memories.

> *When I was doing particular 'heavy work' on my past — remembering my past, flashbacks — I would cut my arms really bad and leave them to bleed and not patch them up.*

Identification of feelings around self-harm

Whilst most of the time the young people harmed themselves in private, the feelings sometimes became so intense for some that occasionally they would harm themselves while others were around. In comparison to the amount and the frequency of harm they would inflict on themselves when they were alone, this was rare.

When it did happen — for example some young people recounted situations when they were with other people which they had found difficult to handle — they would often look for somewhere private (usually the toilet). Though on occasions it would become obvious to others what had happened so that they became a focus of attention, often the self-harm would go undetected. For example young people who had cut themselves would mop up with tissues afterwards and hide the cut under a sweater; or they would take some pills but still act 'normally'. In these situations the young people often felt that they were 'losing it' — that they were no longer feeling logical or rational and that in some ways they were losing control.

> *When I've done it in front of people or gone off to the toilet and done it . . . but I was completely off my head when I did it so I'm not that surprised. I wasn't really thinking straight.*

The young people displayed some uncertainty over whether they could identify the feelings which were present before they were likely to harm themselves. Many of them did recognise some of these: for example, anger, frustration, tension, pressure, memories and flashbacks.

> *It all just blurs into one, the times when I've harmed/hurt myself — there's always been a particular feeling about it and it's always that feeling that's there when you're hurting yourself — a 'buzz'.*

> *I'd just know I had this pressure and I'd get everything ready — the blades, the antiseptic, the gauze, the plaster.*

However, some young people suggested that often they would be unaware that they might harm themselves even while at the same time partially recognising the feelings. One young man, in describing his self-harm and attempted suicides, said that at times *'it just happens'.*

> *I won't know (whether to) until I'm actually doing it or until the feeling goes away.*

> *I never know I'm going to do it. Sometimes I just find myself with a razor blade in my hand. But I know the feeling that I've got when I feel like I'm going to cut up.*

This issue was identified explicitly by one young woman when she talked about the different ways she could end up harming herself.

> *When I started doing it everyday, it got to be really calculated: 'I've got to do it' . . . (it's like) determination — 'I'm going to do this'- (and I think about) how I'm going to do this so people don't see or notice — and it's controlled. I think it through step by step and it kind of comes from 'there' and I just feel I've got to do it, 'I'm going to do it', I feel like a terminator, more controlled. Other times it's more of a hysterical panic thing — grief stricken — not sure what to do, I want to be dead, not sure how or what, and I'd be crying my eyes out and scratching away at my arms.*

A clock ticking

At some moments when the young people were trying to describe their self-harm, it became apparent that they were finding it very difficult to get across in words what it involved. Especially during the individual interviews, this could at times feel like being 'stuck' in the sense that, where 'there are no words', the young people did not feel able to make themselves understood.

When this happened during the group discussions, some of the young people began to attempt to express what was involved visually, thereby investing their experience with more commonality. Although each of them still felt that their experience was unique and thus different from that of others (see Chapter 4: My Own Special Creation) some degree of shared understanding also emerged as the messages were portrayed in an alternative form.

This process also had the effect of moving control of these messages and of understandings of them towards the young people. Thus whilst the young people eagerly debated the similarities and differences between their versions of their experience, this subtle shift of power at times left the group facilitators behind them in clarifying what it meant.

These pictures were described in terms of, for example, feeling persecuted by others and feeling alone. In an individual's life, the build up of such feelings and/or of the effects of what was being said or done to them could at times become so intense that it could feel like a clock ticking. Somehow, this pressure had to be released. Self-harm — in these cases cutting — could then be a way for the young person to regulate and control the feelings.

However, in these circumstances, the need to do it could build up again — the clock would again start ticking away. The self-harm thus offered a form of direct action for the young person which worked and was in some ways guaranteed in its effects — though only until the next time.

One young woman who had not participated in the groups also put this clock ticking theme into words.

> *I feel paranoid. I have this, it's like a clock ticking sort of thing and it goes off in my head — in my arm sort of thing and when I'm cutting it's like the clock is ringing. You know, like the clocks with the bells on the top ... I don't know why but that's what it makes me think of and that's how I feel ... It's like part of it's in my head but the other part's in my arms. It's more or less at once — about a second out. So the head would go off and then the arm.*

Whilst not all of the young people offered this representation of their experience or would necessarily have agreed with it, it is possible to draw out from this description a powerful metaphor for expressing the sense of urgency, need, craving, urge, drive to self-harm.

A clock ticking — releasing the tension.
Adapted from a drawing by group members.

I don't even think about it, it just kind of comes from there, my stomach and I just really <u>want</u> to do it.

Not a craving as such but a need to do it and that goes away until the next time.

It's like a mad feeling in your stomach, it's like pressure all building up and if you don't release it out, are you going to, I don't know, blow up.

It's like a feeling of urgency. I still get it a lot now particularly in the last few months when things have been really difficult again — I've been having nightmares solidly for the last two to three weeks — a dozen a night. I've had really strong urges, like a drive.

It gives me a buzz, like I deserve it. It's like being on a drug, I'm addicted to it because I've been on it most of my life. I'm achieving something.

Hurt/not hurt

As we have seen, because it could serve different purposes at different times for the same individual, it is difficult to generalise or make assumptions about a young person's self-harm. The question of whether or not it hurts when an individual harms themselves is an important one for illustrating this conclusion. Here are two young women describing the different ways in which they might self-harm and the complex rules, feelings and meanings which they attached to their behaviour.

There's a couple of things that happen. Sometimes when I cut up it doesn't hurt at all and it's only when they stitch me up that it hurts even though they numb it. And other times I cut up and it doesn't hurt at all and it feels really numb and I don't feel the stitches or anything ... And then I remember once I felt it hurt but the physical hurt sort of overtook the emotional hurt so I suppose it sort of counteracted it out.

Sometimes it hurt but then I was doing it for different reasons — to see if I could stand it — to make myself do something I didn't want to do (for example burning). Like, 'you've done this, take this' ... if I felt like I deserved it rather than I wanted to do it then it would hurt — because that would be the point of doing it, like punishment ... It depends on what end you're on. If I was thinking it was happening to me then it would hurt but if I was only thinking about my hand, then it didn't feel like that. It depends on whether I felt like the one doing it or the one being done to. Once I'd done it somewhere, it would stay sore for quite a long time, and I wouldn't feel like touching it -because it would hurt. Unless I <u>wanted</u> it to hurt and then I would. If you were the one <u>doing it</u> you'd do it on places which hadn't been done before and if you're <u>having it done</u> it would have to be done on places you'd done before.

Looking for causes — getting all deep and meaningful

In talking about their self-harm one young person stated:

> *(We) need to look at the underlying causes, it's the result of these underlying causes.*

Some of the young people identified strong links between their self-harm, attempted suicide and their past and sometimes more recent difficult experiences and situations. Where this was the case the following experiences were mentioned by the young people:

- Childhood physical and/or sexual abuse
- Bullying
- Rape
- A damaging adult relationship (including emotional and/or physical violence)
- Bad reactions to lesbian/gay sexuality
- Loss
- Suppression of 'negative emotions': for example, anger and sadness. (See Chapter 5: 'A Bad Apple'.)

> *I was abused in a car and sometimes I get flashbacks; it's like I'm reliving it. I jump in front of cars. It just happens.*

> *If I'd been able to get out of the situation that was making me self-harm — the abuse, my feelings, hating myself, and the people who said they cared — I would have given up self-harm, that I was worth something instead of feeling worthless.*

> *I suppose anything which has a large impact on your life, which has been important, which has been destroyed — in all these things there is something which has been destroyed — like your innocence or your safety.*

One young woman talked specifically about the impact of being sexually abused and not being believed by her family, neighbours or the courts.

> *I think my past has a lot to do with me cutting up now basically because it worked then so it works now . . . I know there's a connection there because I remember what was going through my head when I wasn't cutting up. When I was cutting up it was how to get away from the abuse . . . none of that (the abuse) helped and I think that's the reason why I cut up and I think that if none of those things had of happened to me, I wouldn't have started and definitely wouldn't have been carrying on . . . (and then) especially when the verdict of not guilty came in, and people's reactions and I just couldn't deal with it.*

Although for some of the young people this link was in some ways quite clear, they often also emphasised its complexity and sometimes denied a crude causal connection. Indeed, the subtlety and depth of their self-harming behaviour and the functions it served for them meant that often the link was confused and perhaps unconscious or subconscious.

> *When I'm self-harming or overdosing it's not what I'm thinking about, I don't think 'I'll do this <u>because</u> . . .' I just think about what's going on at the time — perhaps it's something that's in the back of me mind though. But, it's not there then.*

> *It's not as simple as — somebody had hurt me therefore I'll try this. I don't think (the development of it) was very straightforward really. I needed to get some kind of release mechanism out and there wasn't any other way I could think of doing it apart from cutting up.*

For the young person concerned it was often clearer and more meaningful to look at the act itself and the immediate gain they got from it (for example, relief) than to try and link it to the past.

Q — Did you know why you did it ?

> *Yes, sort of. But there's also a lot of stuff around questions which I had in my head about why I was doing it . . . I just know how it makes me feel. I don't have like a 100% knowledge about why I do it because part of me just doesn't know. I can only figure out what I think it could be.*

Thus, although these young people often showed great insight into their own behaviour, looking for causes or asking the question "why?" did not always produce very clear answers. Nor was this kind of approach always particularly helpful to them. Often, it seems, it failed to touch what were for them the most important influences and pressures on their behaviour.

> *If you knew why, you wouldn't do it.*

> *I don't think they (workers) understand why I do it and I don't think I could ever explain fully why I do it.*

> *They (the ward) want to get into real depth, they're really into all that stuff. There was this Occupational Therapist, she was great but she left. She was young as well and we could just generally chat about anything without having to get all 'deep and meaningful'. I got a lot out of the work I did with her — more than any of the others.*

> *I don't like delving into why I do it. I find it much more easy just to cut up and then people would shut up about it.*

The problem of searching for causes and the whys of the young people's behaviour was neatly expressed by one young woman.

Some people can't accept the fact that sometimes you just don't know.

The young people's distancing of themselves from deep and meaningful analyses of their behaviour clearly connected with their dissatisfaction with many of the explanations others were producing of its causes. Most commonly such explanations assumed sexual abuse. Also, for a young person who identified as being a gay man or as lesbian or bisexual, or who was exploring their sexuality, it often seemed to be too easily assumed that, for example, self-oppression — their not accepting their sexuality — was at the root of their behaviour.

I don't know, it seemed to be different things at different times. I don't know if there's ever been any one starting point. People have suggested to me I was abused when I was a kid, but I can't see any evidence for it. So I just think it's just different ways of coping at different times with different things.

(Although there's) a lot of pressure to be straight, getting married, my cutting up has never been about my sexuality. It probably happens though.

I got this (assumption that I'd been sexually abused) at school (after cutting up). They didn't ask me if I'd ever been abused, they just blamed it on me dad straight off. They should have asked me straight out. That's why I'm not any good at talking to anyone now about anything. I think that really fucked me up because since then I've just not really said nowt.

Some of these themes and specifically the problems which could arise for the young people from the assumptions others made about them and their past history are developed in greater detail in Chapter 6: 'Not A Clue'. The implications of this evidence for those working with young people who self-harm are taken up again in Chapter 8: 'It's Like There's Two Thoughts Going On'.

Despite the fact that, for many of the young people, looking for causes presented real problems, some could suggest definite causes of their self-harm. This was usually the case when the young person was able to make a clear link between abuse — usually sexual — and the self-harm.

However a distinction could exist here between two groups of young people. On the one hand there were those who, having identified this link, felt that once it had been resolved in some way they would no longer need to self-harm.

But (now) I don't want to self-harm, because I don't feel that pressure in my head anymore.

On the other were those young people who felt that the mere identification of the link, talking about it, getting to the bottom of it, would not in itself lead to their being able or wanting to stop their self-harming.

> *I think quite a bit of it is that you can't talk about it. But I think even if you could would you still do it? And I think I would still do it. I think I would do it because of the relief I get from it.*

It is worth noting that Tantam and Whittaker (1992), in reviewing a study of individuals who repeatedly cut themselves, point out that any insight into the genesis of the behaviour did not necessarily afford relief.

Hope and survival

Despite its appearance of being self-destructive, self-harm could for a young person be 'therapeutic' and in some ways life preserving and could manifest itself as a will to live, to survive. In this sense it might often not be suicidal so much as preventive behaviour.

One of the ways in which this was demonstrated was through the methods for looking after themselves many of the young people adopted as part of their pattern of self-harming. Many of them had their own safety kits of sorts which they would use to help minimise the damage they might do to themselves or to exercise some control over it. For some, this sense of nurturing could be an important (perhaps the first) step in caring for themselves — in taking some control over and responsibility for their self-harm and their own needs — and so deserves to be recognised and even encouraged. (The importance of this is acknowledged by Pembroke, 1994.)

> *I'd just know I had this pressure and I'd get everything ready — the blades, the antiseptic, the gauze, the plaster.*

> *Then I started to get my own bandages and antiseptic so I didn't have to tell my mum I'd done it and get yelled at.*

> *When you cut up and you're getting near to the veins and arteries, it looks like a little muscle sort of thing — not like fat cells. If you don't want to kill yourself then you don't go past that. If you don't want to kill yourself but you want to cut yourself you don't just go in there with a razor blade and just go 'whack' really deeply. You take it bit by bit so you cut a few times on the same spot. Sometimes there's always the option of, if you do it too badly or deeply — you can always go to the hospital or ring an ambulance for yourself.*

> *I choose what I want to use and make sure its sterile and clean ... and I'd make sure I'd got a bandage at hand or a towel or something and disinfectant and everything I needed. I'd have like a first aid kit in my room when I did it on a*

regular basis. I was never really sure what I was going to use. I knew I had a bottle of disinfectant, a packet of cotton wool, a razor blade in a little glass container. Sometimes I didn't care and sometimes I really did.

Some of the young people also talked about ways they had developed for fighting off their urges to self-harm.

I still get urges but I fight it off quite successfully — get out of the house for at least twelve hours, deliberately not do things which involve sharp objects like shaving legs, cutting with sharp things in the kitchen — I can't rule it out. I make sure I'm not in situations where I want to do it and where I can do it.

As we shall see later (Chapter 4: 'My Own Special Creation'), suggestions by other people of things to do instead could miss the essential point for the young person of their self-harming behaviour. Nonetheless, some of them had discovered for themselves some useful ways of redirecting some of the emotions which this seemed to represent.

Each time I wanted to cut up I'm not saying it never bothered me — it did. There were times when I thought I wanted to do it now and I would buy the blades, the antiseptic, gauze and plasters but I'd just sit looking at them and think there are other ways. So I'd get on my mountain bike and just pedal and pedal, or stand under a cold shower or go for a walk, find other ways — punching pillows, standing in the middle of a park and screaming at the top of my voice.

One example of finding other ways not to self-harm was to get involved in creative hobbies, often music or art. Some young people talked, too, about the importance of being with other people in a group, sharing experiences, being able to talk openly about their behaviour and, through such involvements, finding strategies for coping.

Two of the young people also acknowledged that seeing other people harming themselves could sometimes bring home to them what they were doing to themselves. Though perhaps feeling that for themselves it was the right thing to do, for someone else it could seem damaging — that *'they shouldn't have to'*.

In other ways, too, it was important for some of the young people to begin to take control over and even to change their lives, with the result that the control aspect of their self-harm could become less important.

I decided that I wanted to look back at my life and what was going on and thought to myself, do I want to go on cutting myself regularly for the rest of my life? It was down to once a week or a fortnight — do I want to go on doing this, can I control it? Would it make me feel better if I did control it, control other bits, leaving my job, leaving school, go to college to do 'A' levels and go to University.

In addition, some young people could get to a point where they felt that they no longer needed the behaviour — that they could make a choice to rid themselves of it — though, again stopping was never a simple or straightforward decision.

It wasn't like I could just stop — 'the last time' — I just needed to do it less and less.

I really want to get it sorted now — to not have it as part of my life anymore. I'm convinced there's light at the end of the tunnel.

CHAPTER 4

My Own Special Creation

It's society isn't it . . . you've got to be sociable, you've got to fit into their plan and all that, you can't stand out and be individual.

(The self-harm) it just seems to be something that's evolved and grown as I've grown.

Cutting was always a very private, secret and personal thing.

A sense of achievement

Many of the young people interviewed for this study experienced themselves as not being valued, not being worthwhile. They often lacked a sense of purpose, of making a contribution to anything or of being part of something outside themselves.

For young people who were dealing with an array of negative feelings and self-perceptions, self-harm could enable them to feel that they were doing something for themselves and that after all they did have some worth.

> *Self-harm was a way of feeling that I was worth something to myself because I can say 'god, I can control this, how many times I cut, how far I go, where I do it and how I do it'. Nobody can control that — yes they can lock you up in a mental hospital, but they've got to let you out someday. They can only sedate you for so long and it doesn't do any good.*

> *It feels like you're not worth anything because you haven't got a job, you're not helping anyone (family), just getting in their way. Useless.*

> *I never got compliments on what I did . . . no purpose, no contribution.*

These motives, together with the variety of functions which at different times it had for them, could make their self-harm a very special part of their lives. Particularly if it had gone on for a long time and if they felt it had given them something that was helpful, they might desperately cling onto it as a very personal act. For such young people it could then feel part of their identity, part of themselves.

I don't care about it, whether I do it or not, if I do it it's nothing unusual for me, it's normal life . . . it feels like part of me.

But I think if you do it over a long period of time it does — it becomes part of me, part of my life (overdosing on medication, cutting up); a major part of my life. It identifies more with me than not me. When I don't do it it's not the same as when I do it.

Indeed, for some of them, at some points in their lives, self-harming could become a major preoccupation — their main focus point — to the extent that sometimes their life revolved around it.

It's like a ritual.

I'd do it at least once a day, usually four or five times a day — it was like a main focal point in my life — that's when it was the biggest.

Some young people also expressed a strong sense of delight about their 'discovery' of self-harm.

It was new and exciting, great, something amazing.

Others talked of gaining a sense of achievement from it. For those who had been or continued to be abused (physically, sexually or emotionally) it could in some ways feel liberating. It was as if they could take control of the abuse and do it to themselves rather than an abuser or bully doing it to them.

In this context, their attitude to pain was revealing. Many of them suggested that, though the abuse would hurt when someone else was the perpetrator, usually there was no pain when they harmed themselves.

When I was about twelve or thirteen I'd cut up quite badly and had to get it stitched quite a few times. They (my parents) would go apeshit. Then she (my mum) would get a razor and do it to me. It hurt when she did it but when I did, it didn't hurt.

Only when they felt that they should be punished for what they had done wrong were they likely to feel pain. Indeed, experiencing the pain could be one reason for self-harming — because they felt they deserved to be hurt.

The young people could therefore derive considerable pride and sense of achievement from the harm they did to themselves. This might be particularly true if they had had experiences of being marginalised — of being treated like an outsider — since such feelings could be directly related to other negative feelings about themselves, of being bad, evil, dirty.

I took a certain pride in being able to take pain. It was like I was good at something.

It's still the same, you get a buzz off looking at it. Like you've accomplished something if you've got really good ones.

Control and survival

In circumstances where everything else around them seemed to have gone wrong, the self-harm was therefore something which the young people could feel they were able to do for themselves and control. And, because it gave them a sense of purpose and a focus in their life, they often set a time aside for it and would spend long periods doing it.

> *I liked doing that the best then because it was slow and I could really take my time and I was really into what I was doing because it really, sort of, made me feel better about myself when I cut up. So I'd spend hours doing it . . . I could spend up to half an hour doing it. I used to do it at break times and if I didn't have enough time to do it — if I had to have a break — then I'd get some superglue . . . (if I didn't have enough time to finish off) I'd stick the superglue in the grooves and put me shirt down so no-one would see it. So next time I had time to do it, I'd just peel it, also cutting the superglue out so I could do it again.*

Other evidence supports this conclusion. Burstow for example has argued that self-harming gives some women feelings of control over their lives and a sense of strength and success derived from this.

> "Many women who have trouble experiencing themselves as strong or successful find strength and success in self-mutilation. As ashamed as they may be by the mutilation, the truth is that many also take pride in it. They tell themselves that most other people do not have the stamina to do what they are doing; and they are right. They know that others do not have the incredible discipline and fortitude to subject themselves to hour after hour of self-torture. By contrast they repeatedly inflict pain on themselves for hours and emerge tangibly and visibly successful. The wound is there — an achievement, a mark of endurance . . . We need to recognise the importance of the perseverance and what it gives them." (Burstow, 1992: 196)

For these young people, what was also important about gaining a sense of greater control and power in their lives was the feeling that here was something which was theirs.

> *It's mine, it's me.*

These after all were young people who, in various ways, had had their isolation and marginalisation forced upon them. They therefore distrusted other people. They might also feel that they did not deserve anybody else's care or attention — that in some ways they had to do it for themselves. As one young man put it, though some people might use drugs, for him that was no good because it meant relying on others — pushers for example. In his case (as for many of the young people), what seemed to be essential to the activity of self-harming was that it remained very personal and private. He needed no-one else to carry it out.

Secrecy as power

The young people also emphasised the importance of ensuring that no-one else controlled or stopped their self-harming which was for them an expression of rebellion and resistance.

> *It's like saying fuck off to everything.*

For many of the young people, these feelings of being more powerful and in control seem to have been strengthened by the fact that this was an activity which they could keep for themselves, hidden away from other people.

> *I starve myself the day before the day I do it, then I put them (pills) in my pocket and I'll go walking down the street dead normal. Nobody'll tell what I'm doing and I'll have a drink in one hand and I'll pop a handful.*

> *I think that's because people can check you as much as they like but they can't find anything and you can make wonderful excuses as to why you're like that. When you've overdosed you can do it easier. So they don't realise. But the problem is they know what I'm like so they often take me down to Casualty anyway, just to check.*

> *When people found out, then it became defiance. To see if anybody could find out. A competition that nobody knew about apart from me. To see if I could get away with it. To do something people didn't know about. It was more important that people didn't find out.*

In some cases this behaviour was another way of increasing a young person's sense of individuality — by (literally, in many cases) marking them out and making them different. It could therefore be a very effective and in some ways positive strategy of resistance, of retaining a sense of self despite everything else that was going on in their life. However, here again contradictions are apparent. For, by its very nature, their self-harm could also reinforce feelings of being an outsider, of being marginal and alone.

Nor was this vicious and powerful circle likely to be broken by interventions which, however inadvertently, reinforced the young person's image of themselves as outcast. For, as a final irony, when professionals or family did identify and label their behaviour and attempted to control or stop it, the young person might end up feeling like a freak, or being ridiculed or put on public show. They might for example find themselves the focus of shock/horror reactions like: 'How could you do this to yourself?' Or be told to hide their injuries because they were so horrible they would upset other people. Overall the effect could therefore be to further strengthen their sense of marginalisation, as well as to reinforce all those perceptions of themselves described earlier as bad, evil and dirty.

To summarise, many of the young people in this study clearly felt that a great deal in their lives was controlled by others. This might manifest itself through upsetting remarks and comments, through abuse or bullying, through being in an institution or in care. In coping with these experiences, self-harm became a way for the young people of achieving some control for themselves — a means of expressing independence, autonomy and personal freedom. (See Ross and McKay, 1979.)

However, the self-harm could mean more than this, too. In giving a young person this increased sense of power and control — a purpose and an aim — it could in some respects provide a reason to live and so could become preventive (that is, it could prevent worse happening such as suicide). This view was not of course without its problems and contradictions, of which the young people themselves were often (only too painfully) aware. Some of them for example described how self-harm became an addiction, an urge, a craving, a need or compulsion; and how, for the self-harm to continue to give them what they felt they needed from it, it might increase in severity.

Nonetheless, as we have already seen, self-harming could in itself become a strategy for coping and even self-preservation.

> *I don't see it as a _problem_ — now me mum always goes on that it's an illness but I don't see it like that — I don't think it is. I just think it's a thing, just like another part of you, just like a bit of me ... It's just me now, innit. That's how I see it, I class it as me now. It's just mine, isn't it. I would like to cut down and that but I don't think I could ever be totally without it.*

Where their self-harm was having such 'therapeutic' effects, these would seem to have stemmed at least partly from its capacity to make the young people feel more in control, more powerful and more purposeful in their lives.

Cross-infection

Quite commonly the young people faced another kind of response, especially when they were in an institution, which they found unhelpful: that of being prevented or discouraged from mixing with other people who self-harm or attempt suicide in case they encourage each other. In fact, the evidence from this study suggests that such contact could have the opposite effect. One young woman for example talked of how in various ways she and her friend were helping each other to stop self-harming.

As we have also seen, though a young person might feel that they themselves deserve it, they would rarely believe that of someone else. If therefore they saw the things in another person which they hated in themselves, yet at the same time accepted that these characteristics did not make this other person bad, they might be helped to feel less bad about themselves and less different from others — and so less inclined to harm themselves.

Giving it up

Yet it is important to recognise that by this time self-harm may have become very much part of the young people's identity. And that this, particularly when placed in the context of the range of functions which their self-harming has for them, helps to explain why it is so difficult, and frightening, for them give it up.

For some young people the fear of losing it — of not having it around anymore like a trusted friend — is therefore a major issue. ('The pain and blood will always be there for me.' Favazza and Favazza, 1987). Thus Miller (1994) has argued that self-harm can offer a form of security which contains a familiarity and reassurance similar to that of a stable relationship.

Miller goes on to argue that the more others try to separate (the woman) from this relationship with 'the bottle, the drug, the food, the razor, the surgeons knife, the cigarette, the more she clings to it' — an 'us against the world defiance'.

Indeed self-harm may be a very special version of the premise that everyone needs 'their own thing': something which they feel is theirs and special to them and which they feel they can do well. For many people this may be a job, a relationship, their children. Or it may be a creative hobby, a sport or music, something else.

It was argued earlier that these are young people with little or nothing in their lives which they feel is special and through which they can experience success. Thus their resort to an activity which, however inadequate and by definition damaging, may at least offer them an opportunity for getting some of this sense of positive achievement.

> *Most kids feel powerless so they become attached to things — drugs, control, or for girls, having a baby — to mother them like no-one's mothered me. Like doing things for someone. Being worthy of something. Being needed. Everyone needs to feel needed.*

> *I think if I'd ever have had something to actually grab hold of then I don't think I would've (self-harmed) — but I didn't. I'm not quite sure what it might have been. An ideal world where everything that was meant to be was there.*

Alternatives — what alternatives?

During the research, the young people frequently gave examples of suggestions for things to do instead of self-harming which other people — professionals, friends, family — had suggested to them:

- taking Vitamin C instead of overdosing;
- having a bath in lavender oil;
- cycling briskly round the block;

- masturbating;
- putting tomato sauce on their arms instead of cutting;
- watching TV;
- doing twenty press ups;
- ripping up photos;
- playing rugby;
- drawing a picture;
- smashing a mug;
- bashing a pillow.

Though at first sight these could appear to be reasonable in themselves, for the young people they seemed to miss the point. Finding alternatives for them would go against that essential part of their self-harm which defines it as theirs and as something which is *'to myself, for myself'*. As one young woman put it:

> *If you want to self-harm why would you want to do anything else if you can get the real thing?*

Here again was recognition of contradiction and tension in their situation. Though their position might be very tenuous and, from day to day and week to week very variable, the young people might come to a point where they want to stop self-harming. However offering suggestions could still be a problem — precisely because the self-harm was for many of them 'their own special unique creation'. It was something which they could do for themselves in order to exert some control over their life. No-one else could touch or interfere with it. Suggestions for alternatives made by other people were therefore unlikely to be helpful. They would work against the very reason why the young person self-harmed in the first place. They would take the control out of their hands and give it to someone else.

The young people who took part in the group discussions found some of the suggestions made to them for stopping their self-harming quite amusing. For them the people making the suggestions had not really grasped what was involved and *'of course they wouldn't work!'* These reactions further reinforced their lack of trust in professionals and their belief that *'nobody understands'*. At the same time they enabled them to keep something for themselves which nobody was able to *'get into'*.

Though finding alternatives could be useful, the young people frequently felt they needed to define these for themselves. They would also have in some ways to be special to them, through which they could express themselves. And they would need to offer similar rewards to their self-harming.

On the surface, the alternatives which the young people had found useful did not appear all that different from the kinds of suggestions made to them by other people (referred to earlier). However in certain respects, for the young person, these were intrinsically different: they were once again something of their own which were special and which they had found themselves. And essentially they directed their energy into constructive and creative activities requiring individual thought and imagination. Examples quoted included playing the guitar, the drums and the piano. (For more detailed discussion see Chapter 7: 'Keeping The Channels Open'.)

Thus the young person's need to self-harm could become less pressing when they had another involvement which they felt was theirs, which they could control and in which they could get absorbed. This — which could also be an enjoyable job, a comfortable home, a good relationship, a creative activity — could combat those negative feelings on which their self-harm was focussed — feelings like: *'I don't have a purpose in life'; 'I don't contribute to anything'; 'I'm of no value'; 'I'm useless'.*

If I was doing something I really liked and was well into it, I think that would help.

One young woman who spoke of not harming herself for many months said:

Everything's changed. I also have a feeling of being part of something as well.

Moreover, once the self-harm had become part of a person's identity, they might have to make major changes in their life if they were to begin to give it up. Indeed, one young woman talked about changing her whole identity.

Since I've been doing my work and getting on with my life, somehow I've taken on a completely new meaning and a new life, changed my name and lifestyle and area that I live. It just feels now that there's no need to self-harm.

Miller (1994) provides some supportive evidence for such a conclusion. She emphasises for example that, until the individual (woman) can find other ways of feeling strong, particularly in relation to other people, the secret and powerful nature of her self-harm can act as a positive in her life. Indeed, as our research suggests, by generating such feelings of power it can ultimately enable her to survive.

In fact, many of the young people in this study went even further. They even questioned whether their version of dealing with stress was any worse than others which were more sociably acceptable. Commonly cited examples of the latter — smoking, alcohol, drugs — were seen as potentially carrying the still greater risks of liver damage and lung cancer. Though perhaps less true of overdosing, it could be argued that the young people's self-inflicted wounds do heal, often leaving no lasting (physical) damage — especially given the way many of these young people cared for their injuries after they had self-harmed.

In taking up this position, some of them also seemed to be arguing that only when their behaviour was discovered and then defined, controlled and interfered with did their self-harming become a problem. When they were together in the group discussions (rather than in the individualising and isolating interview situation) a small but significant shift occurred in their location of the problem. Increasingly this moved away from 'me' as the problem to locating it elsewhere, for example: in other people's reactions and non-acceptance, poor service provision, and oppressive personal histories.

It was in fact in the group discussions that some of the young people expressed a particularly intense resistance to external definitions of, controls over and interference with their self-harm.

No-one else can control it.

It's all about it not being defined.

In a way we wouldn't want people to understand it.

At some points during the interviews, and again particularly within the group discussions, the young people pushed this argument still further. Some of them asked whether their response might not perhaps be more admirable in some ways than everyone else's out there — that is, whether self-harming might not show a strength of character.

Don't judge it until you've tried it.

Probably the sanest of people are self-harmers . . . maybe we're all normal and you're not.

Some of the young people felt that, in comparison to other young people, they might be more sensitive — and too easily hurt or affected by other people or the situations in which they found themselves. This issue seemed of particular concern to the young men. As is now widely recognised, they are brought up to be tough — and not to allow themselves to be affected by other people's remarks other than by getting angry. The ones who do not fit this stereotype — like many in this study — are therefore likely to feel especially marginalised.

Contradictions and tensions

However, a number of contradictions were apparent within these arguments, and these were recognised by the young people. The tensions surrounding the issue itself, including the young people's own definitions of it, need to be recognised.

Thus, they did want to be understood and to be helped, often despite the rewards their self-harm contained for some of them as individuals. It remained an essentially alienating experience and therefore was seen as not a good thing. Indeed, as all of them acknowledged, they self-harmed because, in the end, they felt *'crap'*.

You're doing it for a reason. (I don't do it) because I enjoy doing it. You may enjoy the feeling you get but you don't enjoy the fact that you're mutilating yourself . . . you don't do it if you've got a rosy life.

Again, they might have wanted (sometimes desperately) to hold onto their 'own special creation' and therefore be resistant to talking about it or having it interfered with. They might feel that their self-harm was done *'to myself and for myself'* and as such was nobody else's business. They might therefore not seek help and might even deny it was a problem. At the same time they might recognise the dangers involved in their self-harming and want to talk about it, be listened to and *'get it sorted'*. They might even long to communicate about it so that they need not be alone with it but could break out of their isolation and marginalisation.

A further contradiction was embedded in the young people's fears about 'interference' — that other people would *'get in on it'*. It was because self-harm was so often 'their own special creation' that they felt it gave them some power. Yet, if they talked about it or sought help in dealing with it they were concerned that it might no longer belong to them but to the people who had asked about it, observed it or come to know about it in other ways. When this happened they then feared that, in losing these forms of behaviour, they would lose control and so perhaps damage themselves even more. The loss of the self-regulatory functions of the self-harm seemed to them to carry potentially frightening threats to their sense of self and of leaving them with a range of unwelcome feelings, fears and memories.

Intervening in the contradictions

The conclusion to be drawn from all this is of course <u>not</u> that professionals, helpers or carers should just ignore self-harm on the premise that it will just go away, or that they should avoid talking about it with the young people. (See Chapter 8: 'It's Like Two Thoughts Going On'.)

However, a very delicate balance needs to be struck between allowing the young person to keep control of their self-harm while at the same time avoiding reinforcing it as simply theirs and thereby ignoring the pain associated with it.

Indeed, precisely because self-harm can become a part of the young person, it is not possible to separate it off from them as an individual and 'treat it' in isolation. This means that it cannot be effectively regulated or controlled — for example, by a range of ingenious behaviourist interventions which treat the behaviour as merely maladaptive and therefore as capable of being unlearnt. For the young person self-harm is not about having an unfortunate, irritating habit which needs to be broken. On the contrary, it is up to workers to think about how they build up trusting relationships which may help young people explore their self-harm and look at different ways of experiencing control.

CHAPTER 5

'A Bad Apple'

The feeling and expression of negative emotions

(Me and my mum) first went for help when I was eight or nine to deal with my mood swings — and getting agitated all the time and me being a bad apple — not that I was, but that's what I thought of myself.

You feel you're disgusting

Many of the words used by the young people when they talked about their self-harm conveyed powerfully negative messages about themselves — as bad, evil, disgusting, worthless, dirty and useless.

It is important to recognise that the young people carried such feelings about themselves around with them since, for many of them, they underlay much of their behaviour towards themselves. Some of them for example saw their self-harming in particular as a way of releasing this dirt, or sense of being evil, since it could enable them to *'throw away all the badness'*.

The term *'a bad apple'* in the quotation above was thus used by one young man to describe how he viewed himself and, importantly, how he was viewed by others when he was a child. Such self-perceptions once again contradict many of the commonsense assumptions about young people who attempt suicide or self-harm — that for example they are manipulative and attention-seeking. In contrast, most of the young people in this study felt bad about revealing their suicidal feelings, their suicide attempts and their self-harm. Because these included shame and guilt, both the actual feelings of being bad and the behaviour which resulted could in fact make their disclosure difficult. A few of them also felt that such disclosure would not only make them feel worse, but might also contaminate others.

You feel that the things you did are so disgusting. You feel you're disgusting and you shouldn't be living because you're so disgusting and you don't want to inflict it on anyone else ... Can't get rid of it. Talking about it makes me feel even more disgusting.

You think no-one wants to come near you because you're disgusting, dirty, worthless.

Clearly, too, the young people feared or even expected that other people would react negatively (particularly to their self-harm, but also to their overdosing) and so would think they were bad, sick or dirty. As one young woman put it:

> *They thought I hadn't come about cutting my arms and I thought if I told them they would tell me to go away and that I was sick, so I didn't.*

One young man reflected on how he was often left feeling bad after talking about his self-harm during counselling.

> *(It's) nerve-racking . . . hard saying stuff — what I've done and hard to put it into words and because it's about feeling <u>dirty</u> and feeling tense and wound up inside — and they just seem to sit there listening and not trying to help to find a way out, a solution. It perhaps makes me feel worse — on my own, feeling dirty around what I've done and what I've said.*

For many of the young people these feelings arose from actually having encountered negative reactions to their behaviour.

> *But then also I know that it's a pretty disgusting thing to do to take a load of pills. It doesn't help when people say you'll go to hell and that you're evil. Perhaps I am going to go to hell, it feels like hell anyway so it couldn't be much worse.*

The links young people made between their self-harming and damaging experiences in their past seemed to contribute to these negative feelings about themselves. Sexual abuse in particular, but also physical violence, bullying, being seen as different and the suppression of emotions, could marginalise them and make them feel like an outsider or alien.

> *Sometimes I don't like being like this . . . because I feel like I'm not part of this world, I'm outside it, an outsider, feel like you're an alien. I thought I had 'rape me' on my head — thinking I was dirty. I kept washing myself all the time, thought I was disgusting, flashbacks, getting picked on.*

One young man talked about having been bullied because of his sexuality and the oppression he encountered because he was gay, and not fitting in to gender expectations of his behaviour.

> *I was different and I became a target for people having a go. It was psychological — the physical bullying didn't really bother me. It was like 'who can you trust?' I was on my own, no-one to talk to. And hearing all this stuff coming out about AIDS and about what they think about people. Bigoted remarks.*

I blame myself

Their past experiences of abuse, bullying, oppression often also left the young people feeling that it was their fault that these things had happened. This is common amongst survivors of abuse who can feel that it was they who had done something wrong or that they must have provoked the abuse or could have stopped it.

I suppose I deserved it really. I couldn't tell anybody because I felt it was my fault, what did I expect? ... I will always think deep down that I could have prevented it, which is true because I could have.

It wasn't always a feeling of not being able to cope that made me cut up. Sometimes after particular abuse had happened I would hate myself for it and thought 'you dirty, lousy scumbag, you don't deserve to live after what you've just done' ... I'd hear voices in my head saying 'you're dirty, disgusting, why don't you kill yourself'. I did feel that I was dirty and disgusting and didn't deserve to live.

I blamed myself for (my dad) leaving and not being the ideal child and having crazy mood swings and being really up and getting angry and frustrated, being hyperactive ... It was blaming me for things that weren't really my fault, but in the end I got to blame myself anyway.

I got beaten up by mum's new husband and by his mum and dad — they thought I was evil — 'Damien the Omen'. I was about three or four. I've asked her why but never got a answer. I blame myself. I was told me mum had high blood pressure because of me.

Why me?

Thoughts in my head, things that had happened to me as a kid. I had a whole load of questions about why it happened, why it happened to me, and my input in it happening. I never did find the answers, it's just what you think was happening.

I blamed myself for a while. Why me? Why was I always getting picked on? What was I doing wrong?

That has an effect on everything — the whole thing — getting fostered out, getting beaten up, thinking I was evil, not being able to do what I wanted, not being able to make decisions and at the end thinking 'why me?' and trying to find the answer and trying to get someone to be straight with me and tell me — that's what made me do it ... Why? What's wrong with me?

Far from being an attempt to manipulate others, self-harming for some young people became a way of trying to change <u>themselves</u>.

Self-abuse is a way of control — to change the way you are to fit in ... cutting — could be self-hate. Taking anger out on yourself ... Thinking it was all my fault and blaming myself. Sexuality — if I could change it then I would. Why am I like what I am?

It could also frequently be a — usually silent — expression of frustration about a difficult situation.

> *It was so disgusting that sometimes I used to hit myself because I was so angry — angry with myself. I wanted things to change, at home, with my family — blaming myself. I still do in a way.*

It was like I deserve it

For some young people the self-harm could also be a way in which they took things out on themselves — an urge for self-punishment arising out of their deep feelings of self-hate.

> *Self-harm is not a medical issue. It's not about being mentally unstable. It has nothing to do with how mentally stable or unstable you are. It has to do with hatred for yourself, feeling that you're not worthy of anybody's love or attention . . . self-punishment. You deserve this, you deserve to hurt. You might not feel it now but you will later, in a couple of hours, and I did.*

> *It used to work. It just relieved the pressure because I used to blame myself for what had gone on in and around me all my life. I couldn't be punished so I'd punish myself. Self-punishment.*

> *I felt like I deserved punishment because I'd been punished most of my life — beaten up by my step-dad, both blokes who abused me, saw their faces pictured in my head. I felt like I needed to be punished — I started to cut my arms. I felt like I deserved it.*

You've done this, take this

> *If I thought I was evil I would have to do it for longer just to prove I could do it . . . It'd get you back for all the things you shouldn't have done . . . I just had to prove I could make myself do it. Sometimes it hurt but then I was doing it for different reasons — to see if I could stand it — to make myself do something I didn't want to do. Like, you've done this, take this.*

The young people's feelings of marginalisation and of in some ways deserving it could be so strong that many of them felt that it was *'right and proper'* that they should be hurt and that they hurt themselves. Rarely however would they think that anybody else deserved it in the way they did.

> Q — Why <u>you</u> then? Hurting yourself?
> *I don't know — it just seems so right — it's right for me — but not for anyone else. It's just the way it is.*

Suppressing negative emotions

Some of the young people acknowledged how hard it was for them to express negative emotions — that is, any emotion which it was difficult for them to <u>feel</u> and/or <u>express</u>. These particularly included crying, getting angry or upset when they were feeling bad. They would then blame themselves for having these feelings or reactions.

When this happened, self-harm could sometimes become a way of feeling bad when, for whatever reason, they were unable to feel these emotions in other ways or express them to someone else.

> *I would hit myself — get mad with myself and hit myself, bit by bit — beating my head on the walls. I did it when I was at school . . . I think self-harm is about being annoyed with yourself especially if you feel like you've got to be punished for everything you do.*

> *I used to hit myself because I was so angry, angry with myself, I wanted things to change.*

> *I was taught I couldn't express myself — that I shouldn't do things. And every time I'd had enough and I raised my voice or shouted, it was like 'what have you been on' and I'd get it in the neck.*

> *You shouldn't be angry. Losing control wasn't human, but being angry was stupid.*

Anger

> *(It was) the anger in me which made me want to do it.*

Anger and frustration were frequently the main emotions which the young people identified as underlying their resort to self-harm. This connection — which was often related to the feelings of being evil, bad, dirty — illustrates how difficult such relatively powerless young women and men found it to externalise their aggressive feelings. As one of the young people quoted earlier pointed out, self-harm for him was about taking anger out on himself. In addition, however, suppressed anger towards others — and about the distressing situations they faced — was also frequently present.

> *A lot of it was about anger — for me it was almost all about not being angry with other people, although I didn't know that at first. But it was so obvious that I was angry. Anger about other people. I used to really hate myself and think it was all to do with me but it wasn't anything to do with me.*

> *It didn't really start like that (angry at other people) not consciously, although I suppose it was the underlying thing right at the beginning but I don't think it happened like that.*

Many of the young people commented specifically on how wrong or even bad it felt for them to take things out on other people or to express their anger towards someone who had done or said something hurtful to them. In some ways, they suggested, it was safer therefore to redirect these feelings of anger onto themselves.

> *I don't like taking things out on other people, that's why I take it out on myself.*

> *Self-harm . . . a way of getting your <u>anger</u> out as well — all those feelings out. I just did it once at first and thought I'm not going to do it again . . . just like, get it out, but then I was just getting really down and feeling low all the time and if people would have a go at me, I wouldn't argue back or anything. It hurt me, I would just think why are they having a go at me?*

> *You put the blame on yourself because if you just take what people say and just walk away and don't do anything you've still got it all going around in your head — you've not resolved it.*

> *Like if someone said something which done me head in — instead of like going and belting them that's not right — I would hurt myself instead of hurting them.*

Thus, through harming themselves, the young people could find a way of releasing such feelings of anger and annoyance. One young woman described how cutting was her preferred choice of self-harm because it enabled her to 'lose it' and to lose her temper.

> *You can do loads with cutting — you can lose control. You can't lose your temper with a cigarette, but you can with cutting. Cutting was good because you could do it all over the place, you can really freak out. There is more control in biting and burning, and more <u>spontaneity</u> about cutting.*

These comments begin to convey how self-harm feels for some young people. It may also explain how something which appears to others to involve loss of control can become for the young people a way of gaining control. Specifically, it may be concerned with expressing certain difficult emotions in a more controlled and safer way, in order to prevent them from getting expressed elsewhere. Its potential usefulness for expressing such emotions may also explain why, as suggested above, cutting was often the most popular form of self-harm and the one which was most eagerly talked about.

At the same their self-harm and the various ways in which they used self-harm could for some of the young people also be a veiled way of expressing these emotions. As one young woman put it:

> *I just like to get one over on them instead of them getting one over us.*

One of the commonest ways in which this could happen was through the young people keeping their behaviour secret from others, such as their family and professionals.

Sometimes anger was actually expressed through fantasies or daydreams about getting back at people who had hurt them (abusers, bullies). For a few of the young men and women this could sometimes occur during the actual act of self-harming.

It was like it wasn't towards me, it was towards them.

I don't feel like I do it toward myself even though there's the scars there. It doesn't actually hurt. I don't feel no pain, and that's why it doesn't feel like it's toward myself, it's towards them (my abusers) and it's always been like that . . . coz there's a lot of anger there and it relieves it . . . coz I couldn't get them any other way.

It could also involve thinking about death.

If I did die I would want someone to tell him (my dad) why I'd done it.

The suggestion that, for some young people, self-harm has the function of expressing anger was first made in Chapter 1 ('A Few Hours Break'). It will be considered again in Chapter 7 ('Keeping The Channels Open') when possibilities for service provision are examined, and in particular the young people's ideas for anger or rage rooms which would allow them to vent their anger in a safer way than self-harming.

Crying/getting upset

Another set of commonly suppressed emotions about which some young people felt bad was sadness, crying and getting upset.

I made a promise, a policy to myself about not getting upset or crying. I had to keep it forever more.

It (feeling bad) was just wrong and that was it. It was okay to feel okay. I was outwardly all right until it was okay <u>not</u> to feel okay and then I just didn't know what to do. It was like being give permission to feel bad but not knowing how to do it. You're allowed to feel bad but not to do anything about it.

If I cry then that's worse. If I cry I find I go through a mad stage where I just do it (harm myself) all the time. I just don't like crying. It's like you've let something go, like. What the fuck did I cry for?

For these young people harming themselves could be a way either of feeling bad and sad when they were unable to express these inter-linked emotions in any other way; and/or of punishing themselves for feeling like that and particularly for wanting to express such feelings directly — for example by crying. However, as we have seen before, self-harming could then become part of a vicious circle, with young people also often talking of how bad, guilty and embarrassed they would feel after harming themselves or overdosing, and of how this behaviour could reinforce their negative feeling towards themselves.

I didn't analyse it at all I just hated myself and hated myself for doing it but I'd do it anyway and then I'd feel a bit better.

But afterwards you feel worse because of it — bad — then perhaps do it more — justifies it. But at same time perhaps relieved . . . I think afterwards when you've seen what you've done — that's probably what gives you the bad feeling.

At first it was like a release I suppose and then I felt good after it. After a day or so I'd feel really dirty — because of what other people think.

Reinforcing feeling of badness through various forms of intervention

Many service responses and other forms of help could further reinforce or perpetuate these feelings of badness and the need for self-punishment. They could be experienced by the young people as thinly disguised, if unconscious, forms of punishment in themselves. Thus some classic behaviourist interventions were described by one young woman as:

All that reward and punishment crap.

Some of the young people who had experienced these techniques felt that they had as a result become more angry and wound up.

Many of the young people anyway had a difficult time in hospitals (casualty and psychiatric wards), feeling that they had been made to feel bad and guilty about their self-harm.

They made me feel like I was using up a bed.

(They made me feel) that I was a waste of time and space.

Another young woman described overhearing a member of staff in a casualty ward suggesting that she should have her stomach pumped after an overdose to 'teach her a lesson'.

Enforced stopping of the self-harm

Where young people had been unable to release their anger and frustration because they had been prevented from self-harming, their feelings could be exacerbated and made more acute. In these circumstances, the damage they might do to themselves through their self-harm could be worsened.

(Feeling really controlled and being constantly watched) made me more and more angry and more and more pissed off about life.

Some of the young people who had experienced abuse — which, as we have seen, might well underlie their feelings of being bad — suggested that such control and punishment in some ways replicated their experiences of the abuse.

In general, isolating the young person from their environment in these ways and treating them as the problem was liable to reinforce their feeling that *'it must be me'* — that *'there must be something wrong with me'*. Any resistance to treatment which was then punished or pathologised could have the effect of further reinforcing both the young person's sense of being bad and their isolation and marginalisation. The result then was to further increase their distrust of the helping services. And this in turn could set in motion a repeat trip along the path of self-harm and/or suicide: feelings of self-hate, distrust of the system, suspicion (*'who can I trust?'*); and feelings that *'I'm bad and no-one can help me'*.

Finally, no matter how long the cycle had been going on, this pattern of responses could end up being labelled and so stigmatised as :'chronic self-mutilation', 'personality disorder', 'severe impairment', 'a failed case'. As one young woman put it:

It's like they've given up on you.

However, this same process could also be reinforced by rejection of the young person and their behaviour. This might be expressed by a decision to 'move the young person on'; by passing the buck; by such responses from the helper as: 'you can't come here if you continue to damage yourself', 'promise me you won't do it again'; or 'you need to make a contract to stop self-harming'; or by expulsion from a day centre or hospital ward because of their self-harming or suicidal actions.

These problems in the services' attempts to help the young person are explored further in the next chapter, 'Not A Clue'.

CHAPTER 6

'Not A Clue'

Young people's opinions on negative service provision and intervention.

Negative images — and responses

Many of the young people commented that they had never experienced a positive reaction to their behaviour or received support from those who were confronted with it. Significantly (and ironically) one young woman said:

> *I don't think I've had a good reaction yet. I think I'd die of shock if I did get one.*

If, as is often assumed, their repeated suicidal behaviour and self-harm really is motivated by a desire to receive attention and get a reaction from others, why, given this absence of perceived positive responses, do these young people continue with such behaviour? On the other hand, what if the behaviour stems (as often seems wholly or partly to be the case) from a need to be punished because that at times is what they feel themselves to deserve (for example because of continuing abuse)? As we have already argued, many of the helping/treatment strategies adopted may then serve only to reinforce the young person's negative feelings about themselves. This suggests that the young people's self-harming behaviour has many more meanings than the responses it is receiving are assuming or allowing for.

Many of the problems with service interventions which the young people identified seem to have been rooted in part in this crucial lack of understanding on the part of those services. In particular, helpers seemed to appreciate neither what the repetition of self-harm and suicide attempts meant for the young person nor the functions it had for them. More specifically, many of the traditional clinical responses to the young person's behaviour seem to have been based on versions of behaviour modification and behaviour reinforcement — even though paradoxically such treatment strategies could actually reinforce many of the feelings and experiences which perhaps underpinned the self-harming behaviour.

For example, because the assumption was made that the behaviour was attention-seeking or manipulative, it might be ignored or minimised. As a result, the young person's feelings of not being heard or listened to, of being marginalised and of being unworthy and undeserving of care could then be reinforced.

Alternatively, it might be assumed that the behaviour was a learnt, maladaptive coping strategy and so for these reasons was manipulative and attention-seeking. The behaviour might then be punished in some way (albeit unconsciously or unintentionally) with the result that reinforcement was given to the young person's feelings that they were bad, dirty and evil and deserved to be punished. (See Chapter 5: 'A Bad Apple'.)

> "There is no place for punishment or criticism of self-harm, however much of a relief it may be for the staff to express these feelings." (Tantam and Whittaker, 1992: 458)

One particularly important failing of the services identified by the young people were the breaches of the trust which they may have built up with a worker or other professional. These might take the form of 'grassing' (for example, talking to their GP about them and their self-harm) as well as, against their will, being discharged after they had harmed themselves, being sent to hospital or being sectioned. These criticisms emerged most strongly from one of the group discussions, when the young people were emphasising the importance of such trust and that, once it had been lost or broken, *'that's it — it can never be regained.'*

The young people also identified two other major problems with the services: the forms of medical interventions they encountered, for example in hospital; and attitudes which had failed to recognise or understand their behaviour or their experiences.

Indeed, one young man felt that it was not his self-harm as such which was the problem but his negative and punitive experiences of the medical profession and other helpers.

> *It's not the doing it that's bad, it's the way you're treated.*

For, not only did the young people want their self-harm and suicide attempts to be taken seriously. They also wanted to be seen as a whole person rather than just having their behaviour become the focus of attention.

> *(Some counsellors) see self-harm as the problem, but as long as I have these things in my head I'll still be doing it.*

Experiences of hospital

Some of the young people who had spent time in hospital were particularly critical of what it had to offer because of their experience of being sectioned, restrained or put in seclusion as a means of treating them and their behaviour.

> *I got caught up in the system, got sectioned. It made it worse. They wouldn't even let me home to get anything, it felt like I was a prisoner, just breathing down my neck ... that's my biggest dread — that happening again. I'd rather be dead than*

that happen again. It made me feel that I'd done something really wrong — that I couldn't be trusted. Complete punishment, being forced to do everything. Stand watching me taking all the tablets . . . I would kill myself if I ever got sectioned again. I would find a way. I couldn't get through it again.

Seclusion room, that was awful, it felt like I was in prison. Treated me really bad, giving me injections, it was making me worse . . . I was a 'nuisance to society'. I was still smacking the walls. I don't think it did me any good, locking me up 'for my own safety'. I think it was making things worse because I was all on my own and I was frightened. It just felt like they could do nothing for me . . . Secure ward, ECT. Lock up ward. I hadn't done anything wrong. They shouldn't have to restrain you all the time and give you injections. They should try and understand why you do these things.

I thought I was fairly in control before I was sectioned and then I went rapidly downhill during that time I was in hospital. That's why it was the wrong environment. I didn't have any space at all and it felt like a prison.

I think suicide is about restraining of the mind and not being understood properly and putting you in prison or secure units or whatever restrains you even more — physically as well, and then you apparently get beaten up and bullied in prison as well.

Many of the young people were thus very critical of the way they were watched and observed whilst they were in hospital. In fact, they were generally unhappy with situations in which they felt they were controlled since, in a number of ways, this could make them feel worse about themselves. By, in some respects, replicating traumatic experiences they had faced before in their lives, it could contribute to the feelings which had prompted their suicide attempts and self-harm in the first place.

Feeling really controlled . . . Last time I was in they wouldn't let me go out to the shops, I had to have two nurses with me. I wasn't allowed to go to the flat to see my cats. They constantly watched me. It made me more and more angry and more and more pissed off about life. And abuse is about being controlled as well because abuse is about them controlling your body and not letting you control your own.

It was the worst time in my life because it was when I was in hospital that I remembered something else that'd happened to me when I was a kid. (It was a) similar experience — being locked up, not being allowed out and not having any privacy or anything.

These experiences of being controlled and of in various ways feeling punished thus meant that, for some young people, the experience of hospital actually increased the likelihood of their harming themselves again.

*Yes, like having everything done for you. That kind of environment makes you
react so badly that you just want to do it more — they might give a shit about why
but they're not allowed to really. They just patch you up, deal with it. My friend
who'd been in hospital after cutting wrists agreed with me — like afterwards you
just want to go out and do it again.*

*It didn't help — it just got worse when I went in. When I first went in I did stop
for a few weeks but then started again. You just see loads of people sitting in the
corridors rocking. I was only seventeen. Then I just started popping all the time
and cutting (in the hospital). My arms are a state now through being in there —
they weren't as bad before. There's nothing ever to do — if you're bored or if you
get really annoyed.*

Many of the young people felt that it had taken a great deal of courage for them to take
themselves to their doctor or to a hospital casualty ward, particularly given how hard they
tried to keep their self-harm secret and their difficulty generally in talking about it to others.
As we have seen, there could be a variety of reasons for this reluctance to go public.
These could include:

- *feeling like you're not worthy of anyone's attention;*
- ambivalence about whether they wanted or needed help;
- embarrassment;
- feeling bad about what they had done;
- being unsure of the response they would get.

The young people thus rarely sought help from the medical services for their self-harm —
and then felt when they did that they were not treated seriously.

*Cutting was always a very private secret personal thing. One of my friends knew
about it but hadn't seen it. Once I cut myself and I cut too deep and scared myself
and I left it for a few days. It still wouldn't stop bleeding and it looked really nasty
so I thought I'm going to have to do something so I asked my friend if she'd come to
Casualty with me. Again I walked out. I felt incredibly patronised like 'A
beautiful young girl like you, you're obviously intelligent, why would you want to
do something like this?'; and 'Are you just trying to get some attention, or what are
you trying to do?' I was so enraged and I just thought you just don't understand
how much time and soul-searching it took me to get myself down here and I walked
away several times just on the trip there. My friend said if you thought the cut was
bad enough then it must be bad enough, you really ought to go, and she hadn't
even seen it . . . That's the only time I've contacted the hospital and I'd never do it
again.*

The young people who had found themselves in hospital after a suicide attempt were also in some despair about whether or not they would contact the hospital services if the situation recurred. Following her experience in a psychiatric ward, for example, one young woman had been left feeling that she would never again contact the hospital services regarding her suicide attempts.

I still think that the completely wrong place for someone who's feeling suicidal is a psychiatric ward. I would have rather been in prison. I didn't feel at all safe. I don't think I would have continued attempting suicide if I hadn't ended up in hospital . . . I think they just thought I felt sorry for myself. It felt like they were punishing me for it. I think they were doing it to teach me a lesson — they did teach me a lesson now — that I'd never step a foot back onto one of those psychiatric wards. It doesn't mean that I'm not going to attempt suicide — it just means that I'm not going to get caught unless I'm dead and then it'll be too late.

With the lack of any accessible alternative crisis support in the community, going to hospital may in fact be the only option for someone in a desperate situation. As one young man put it:

The whole community thing is just a myth.

However, fear and negative experiences in the past may mean that many young people will not seek any help when they have put their lives at risk.

I have taken a load of pills and not gone anywhere. I did feel ill but I was too scared to get it checked out in case I ended up in hospital.

The young people recounted a range of other experiences which had contributed to their lack of faith in hospital care. These included:

- feeling that they were being lectured or told off;
- being patronised;
- not having their wishes respected;
- for young women, being put in a mixed-sex ward and not having a choice of seeing a female member of staff;
- being given drugs which *made me more agitated*;
- feeling *processed like a number*;
- being *threatened* (for example, staff *talking about stomach pumps*);
- being restrained;
- not being given the time and space to talk about their situation.

When you do it you get all these lectures — why did you do it? . . . and why didn't you come and see us first and tell us? . . . and when you do try and do those things you still don't get treated right so you just think 'what's the point?'

They made me feel that I was using up a bed and a friend told me afterwards that she'd heard them saying in Casualty that it'd teach me a lesson if they gave me a stomach pump.

Treated like shit. They were really laying into me saying I was wasting someone's bed, just a waste of time. They didn't listen, didn't take notice of what I said. I tried to tell them why I did it.

Many of the young people had particularly strong feelings about psychiatric wards and day hospitals. They saw these as being concerned only to keep them alive and to make sure that they did not hurt themselves, attempt or commit suicide whilst under their care.

They just seemed to be offering to keep me alive.

All they were bothered about (on the ward) was that I hadn't killed myself and that they'd managed to stop me killing myself. As long as you don't kill yourself when they're in charge of you, they don't care.

Treatment and its effects

The young people were often critical too of the specific techniques aimed at preventing their self-harming and suicidal behaviour which they had encountered. In general they felt that they were liable to be treated as 'brain dead' or stupid; that such treatment did not take them seriously and belittled their experience. It also failed to recognise what their behaviour gave them and why they needed to do it; and again was often punitive. Finally, as we have already seen, the medical techniques used on them could have the effect of breaking trust between them and those who were treating them.

At the same time, the young people also believed that they could *'see right through these techniques'* and that they could generally find ways around their methods so that their self-harming behaviour could carry on. Even when they wanted to stop harming themselves therefore, they generally concluded that the techniques being used in their treatment would not work. For example, they expressed strong views about contracts.

There's so many rules and contracts. I hate contracts, if you do this you're out. Or they'll refuse you treatment — but they don't give you treatment anyway!

I go against them (contracts) because I know I can't help it. I can't just stop cutting myself like that, it's like a drug. 'If you don't cut yourself we'll help you and if you do, we won't help you' and I think that's wrong to be honest, totally wrong. It shouldn't happen.

Contracts — I never listen to it anyway. You have to sign it and all that; I think it's weird they don't do it with anyone else . It's pointless — I still do it anyway.

In some cases written agreements between clients and workers may be useful. However, for these young people the emphasis would need to be on contracts which were binding on the staff or institution rather than just on the young person. For example not rejecting or moving a young person on because of continued self-harm (Tantam and Whittaker: 1992).

Specific, more explicitly behaviourist techniques which some of the young people had experienced were similarly condemned — for example programmes of reward and punishment. These were after all based on assumptions about the possibility of self-harm being unlearnt — for example, if at the very least it was not given attention, or if some form of punishment was imposed, or if the young person was rewarded for not having harmed themselves for a while.

Not surprisingly perhaps, such programmes did not seem to have worked for a variety of reasons. Thus, a young person might pretend they had stopped self-harming *'to make it look good'* while secretly continuing to do so.

> *Reward and punishment crap — I've had that in hospital — it doesn't make you feel any better. You make it look like it does for their benefit so you can get out of the place.*

Or, because they were annoyed and angry at feeling controlled, they might harm themselves anyway to express their frustration and dissatisfaction.

> *I think you do it more to make them leave you alone.*

In addition, as we have seen, if a young person did stop before they are ready and without the underlying feelings being dealt with, they might eventually harm themselves even more seriously.

Thus, as Ross and McKay (1979) have pointed out, the techniques used by services and staff for punishing cutting were often as innovative and varied as the techniques used by self-harmers for injuring themselves. However they also conclude that not only were these corrective measures impressively unsuccessful but that paradoxically they might actually help to promote the behaviour.

The notion of giving an individual <u>less attention</u> when they harm themselves is also rooted in assumptions about attention-seeking: that for example the behaviour is prompted/stimulated by the responses it receives.

Actually withdrawing medication or limiting the number of tablets given to an individual in order to cut down the risk of their overdosing has sometimes been cited as a possible method of reducing the incidences of suicide and attempted suicide (see Hawton and Catalon, 1987; Harrington and Dyer, 1993). However, many of the young people in this study expressed dissatisfaction with this approach, again seeing it as another way of taking control away from them. Some of them did indeed want to be able to give away their pills to staff when they thought that they might go too far. This, however, was different from their being prevented access to medication, especially when they knew that if they really wanted to, they would find a way of getting drugs or razors.

I hate that, they do that with sleeping pills. I'm allowed one a week and I have to take it in front of them at 3pm. I just don't find it works. I think it just winds you up. When I've been on tablets and overdosed I've never taken their tablets — or maybe just the once. I take me own tablets. If they gave me more I don't think I'd do anymore than I was doing anyway.

As Ross and McKay have pointed out (1979), the kinds of behavioural programmes encountered by these young people may have embodied externally imposed adult — or other authority — inspired treatment regimes which overtly seek to control every aspect of the patient's life. In the context of the evidence presented on the power over their lives which young people can exert through their self-harm, it is hardly surprising that such techniques so often failed them.

The young people often also expressed concern and frustration about being moved on because of their behaviour. Here again they were often made to feel that they were being punished or rejected and/or that they couldn't be helped. And again, too, these responses seemed to lack any recognition or understanding of the meaning of their behaviour for them. Some evidence also emerged that, once a young person had been moved on, their self-harm might often increase in frequency and severity, suggesting that in relation to self-harm, services need to operate some form of explicit non-rejection policy.

When I was discharged they said I'd been abusing the system by going into hospital for my own safety, they kicked me out. I've been kicked out of places loads of times, hospital wards.

They never really ask the important issues about why I do it . . . that's the system . . . sometimes when you cut yourself in hospital you get kicked out, for what you did.

For some of the young people one example of being moved on was being referred from one worker to another. This meant that they again had to repeat their story before they could start getting support.

I don't know whether to trust people plus, like, I've had to explain the same thing to loads of different people — 'passed on' — and it's like dredging things up that you're thinking about and then you have to go home to your environment with all these thoughts.

Counselling and therapy

The young people also had some mixed feelings about counselling and psychotherapy. These, they felt, ought to be able to provide them with an environment in which they could explore their underlying feelings. However in practice this kind of support was in their view frequently denied to them on the grounds that talking about it might make it worse. This was particularly likely to happen if they were seen as either unable or unwilling to stop harming themselves and/or attempting suicide.

> *Some people get the impression that if I talk about some of these things that I'm going to do something like that afterwards. A psychotherapist wouldn't accept me because of what I might have done afterwards, that's why they wouldn't accept me, because of my behaviour and they thought it might make me worse. I think that's wrong.*

At the same time, when receiving counselling or therapy, some young people could be left very frustrated by the limitations of time and the other boundaries this could entail.

> *(Self-harm) helps relieve tension and pressure until you've got someone to listen and not say 'ok, you've had an hour's counselling now, I'll see you next week', because you feel like you're being rejected and that you've got a time limit.*

This of course does not mean that counselling or therapy is not appropriate for young people who repeatedly attempt suicide and self-harm. Rather, it may imply that any one-to-one support they are offered needs to emphasise flexibility of contact. Perhaps even more importantly, it needs to ensure that they are receiving additional forms of regular support which are complementary to the counselling or therapy. And counsellors or therapists will also need to recognise and accept that many young people will not be willing or ready to look at the underlying issues of their self-harm — and that this does not necessarily represent failure.

Other services, unhelpful attitudes

A lot of the criticism the young people made about different services was to do with the attitudes shown towards them by the workers. Thus the suggestions about things to do instead of self-harm (which were listed in Chapter 4) were felt to be unhelpful because they were experienced as controlling. Other unhelpful attitudes included people making assumptions about young people or not allowing them to express their feelings. These were attitudes experienced by the young people across a broad range of services, both statutory and voluntary.

For example, many of the young people saw the Samaritans as a potentially useful service, particularly because it was open twenty four hours a day and was therefore directly accessible to them. And outside the actual research interviews positive views were expressed about the help the Samaritans had given them. However, the service was criticised by some who felt disappointed in the response they had received which in their view had been varied and unpredictable. Experiences like these meant that, if the need arose, some young people would not use this service again.

(I was) thirteen or fourteen years old when I was locked in the house, I rang the Samaritans. I'd seen the number and I thought they'd be someone to talk to because that's what it said. I rang back four times in about six weeks and then the fifth time I rang they asked me if I'd rung before and my name. I hadn't really told her much but I started beginning to talk about the abuse but they said they'd have to start limiting my calls. That would've been the first time I told anyone. The feeling I got was that they didn't believe me. I never rang again. It was like they thought I was just out for attention.

I did phone the Samaritans a few times but they were just awful. I'd just say I felt better but I didn't and the second time I started crying and he said 'I'm not doing a very good job of cheering you up then?' . . . and they asked me if I had a boyfriend . . . (They were) not listening to what you're saying, just trying to make you feel better and cheer you up — I don't think that's their place. It was like 'let's not listen to a word you're saying, let's just try to make you feel better'.

It seems significant that even an experienced, respected and widely used agency such as the Samaritans can be perceived by young people as failing to hear what they are saying. This is not simply to criticise the Samaritans — 42nd Street is only too aware of the demands of offering effective telephone support to young people. But it does highlight how crucial the attitudes of professional workers and other helpers are to young people's perception of being properly heard. The young people frequently referred to comments made to them and the attitudes and assumptions underlying these which they had found particularly unhelpful. These could include, as the last quotation reveals, assumptions about a young person's (hetero)sexuality, and a failure to accept and work with a young person's negative feelings.

Other misunderstandings or points of tension among service providers emerged from the research. One might result from a young person not having their changing moods and emotions accepted. Another might stem from prescriptions or expectations of what they might be feeling or needing based on assumptions about the intrinsic opportunities and potential of 'being young'. One young person was told both by her mother and by nurses that she shouldn't have any problems.

Plus they tell you how you should feel not how you do feel. Like I say I've done something good the day before and then the day after I don't feel too good . . . (and they say) 'You should be feeling great'.

Or a young person's appearance might be the focus of attention.

A beautiful young girl like you . . . why would you want to do something like this?

Alternatively, on the assumption that a young person should, could or would want to stop harming themselves, they might be told: 'Promise me you'll never do it again' — even though, whether or not a young person agrees to the promise, their behaviour is unlikely to alter other than perhaps by being driven still further underground or becoming still more secretive.

You've got to want to stop self-harming. It's no good people saying 'you've got to stop, it's not doing you any good and one of these days you're going to kill yourself' because that's the idea ... If you do self-harm you can't control how you feel. Do-gooders who say 'you've got to stop before you go too far'. Come on and get a life, this is what it's all about.

As emphasised in other chapters, a concentration on stopping the self-harm as the main measure of success can frequently be unhelpful. It may not be based on an adequate measure of how a young person is feeling about themselves since, even if they have not harmed themselves for a while, the feelings which have driven their self-harming may be as intense as ever. In addition, as one young woman put it :

It wasn't like I could just stop, 'the last time' — I just needed to do it less and less.

This again illustrates how problems in intervention often result from a crucial misunderstanding of the meaning and functions of the behaviour and the partial control that young people exercise over it.

It's like a release mechanism which it is ... it is for me and it works and no psychiatrist can disagree with me because it does work but they've never known what to say to you because they're all in their little worlds, like 'no you shouldn't do this' and 'it could be fatal'. But if you know what you're doing then it's not fatal if you don't want it to be. Do you know what I mean?

Another frequently expressed difficulty was the tendency of professionals to oversimplify, categorise and label the young person's behaviour. Though the pressures under which many staff were working were appreciated, ultimately this too was still seen as unhelpful.

Professionals, staff, they see it too black and white ... especially the medical profession, putting you in a pigeon hole. They don't see or appreciate the differences. There are a lot of reasons why people do it. I don't think doctors have got the time to try and understand, so they've got to pigeon-hole you in a way.

(The) diagnosis started off with being 'withdrawn' when cutting. When I started cutting they said I was depressed and then it was manic depression and then a while after that they stuck 'suicidal' on me and then I had split personality, schizophrenia and MPD (multiple personality disorder). I think that's about it ... convenient label, 'they're just mad', and then you don't have to think about why.

Some of the young people did acknowledge that on occasions their behaviour could be a form of communication, especially about their need for care and attention. Nonetheless, common perceptions of its being attention-seeking and manipulative were on the whole regarded as undermining them and belittling their complex experiences.

> *(I think they saw me) the same as they do now — they all think it's for attention. I don't think it is, because you wouldn't go if you didn't get caught because you have to go once you've been caught, because otherwise you just won't be left alone.*

> *Manipulative is the wrong word. I don't think it's a very good word for it because that makes it sound very cold and very calculating. It's more than manipulating, its being in a really bad state. Manipulative makes you sound like you're a bitch and you 'want' something. Like 'I want this' . . . I feel so ashamed that I did it. I feel so stupid actually. I don't like anyone knowing. I try to laugh it off.*

> *I think people who say that attempted suicide is manipulative really haven't got a clue what's going on and they've just got to say something to make themselves feel better and it's just an easier cop out, the system is. It's just saying 'manipulative little cow', 'attention-seeking little bitch'.*

It was the way they asked

In addition, many of the young people felt that they had not been given the time or space to talk about their behaviour and the feelings which underlay it. One young woman talked about her experience after having made a suicide attempt.

> *(They) asked me why did I do it. I said I wasn't going to tell them. It was the way they asked . . . mixed sex ward. Male psychiatrist . . . was quite aggressive — 'why had I done it'. If someone asks you like that, you don't tell them. Maybe it was on my records (that I'd done it before) . . . they think that you can suddenly switch on to your feelings and tell them — it's too clinical. They told me in hospital that I wasn't helping myself by not speaking and that made me clam up even more . . . it was all so clinical — there wasn't enough time, 'your turn to go to see the shrink next' and you'd have to go and tell them and I couldn't operate like that. I did know why I was taking the pills but I just wasn't ready to tell them . . . I was too scared to tell them why.*

The Introduction outlined two common kinds of professional medical reaction to young people who repeatedly attempt suicide or self-harm. One, it seems, is to attach imposing psychiatric labels to those who display certain recognised symptoms of 'mental illness'; the other, whilst in some ways allowing the young person to escape a psychiatric career, involves having their experiences minimised.

My GP — never once asked me about it, although he knows about it. I think he should ask, I think it's part of his job really. Perhaps he's hoping that if you ignore it, it'll go away, but it doesn't.

(Professionals were) very scornful, very negative. Mum took me to doctor and he said 'Don't worry loads of people do it'.

Many young people had thus experienced the medical profession as being of little help in relation to their self-harm. Psychiatry, they felt, did not include self-harm as an illness in itself with the result that often no help was made available. Professionals were then seen as 'passing the buck' for their care, often by simply moving them on.

(The) CPN said they can only see people who are 'mentally ill'. People who self-harm aren't seen as mentally ill but a problem is a problem.

This left many of the young people who self-harmed feeling at the 'bottom of the heap'. In one of the group discussions, the young people talked about how they and their self-harm were seen as the *'bad seeds'*, the *'worst of the bunch'* and the *'tip of the iceberg'*. They saw this kind of reaction as being widespread, including amongst other young people.

Generally therefore, the young people felt that they were not believed by many professionals and so, once again, ended up being marginalised.

I told the doctor that I was going to cut my throat but he didn't believe me. He just said he'd arrange an appointment for me. It took a lot of guts to say that to someone. Didn't take notice of the crisis at the time . . . I went out and did it afterwards.

CHAPTER 7

'Keeping The Channels Open'

Young people's views on the possibilities of positive support and services

As we have seen, the young people in this study made a number of explicit and strong criticisms of their treatment by 'the system' which could well leave the services dealing with them, workers and other carers feeling that 'nothing we do will be right' or 'we can't win'. One result of this could be to produce or fuel therapeutic pessimism in this whole area of practice.

It is true that some of the young people (particularly those who had experienced punitive hospital care) were quite pessimistic about the likelihood of conditions changing for the better. At the same time, they felt that trying to bring about some change was so important that it was *'worth a go'*. In fact this was often cited by the young people as a reason for agreeing to be interviewed.

> *I really want to see something positive being done and if my experience can help something positive to come out, and to be able to do something with it then that's good. I think __anything__ would be really good.*

In another way too, some of the young people's responses were far from simply negative. When given an opportunity, they could be both thoughtful and articulate about possible alternative ways of supporting themselves and other young people who self-harm or attempt suicide. Indeed, the substantial agreement existing amongst them on many of these issues contained some important implications and recommendations for future service developments, including awareness-raising and training for workers and carers.

The material in this chapter is presented in three parts:

- Examples given by the young people of small but significant positive experiences of the services and the support they had received.
- The kind of services the young people thought should be offered.
- The kind of attitudes the young people felt would be more appropriate.

POSITIVE EXPERIENCES

Friendships; relationships

> Now I've found the best thing to do if I really want to cut myself is to go and find my boyfriend. I don't always tell him that I want to cut myself because it really freaks him out but I just ask him to cuddle me for a while, until I feel all right again. It _doesn't_ stop me _wanting_ to do it but it stops me actually doing it ... it kind of creates a haven like cutting myself does. I don't think about what else has gone on.

> Luckily the day after, someone from the group here phoned up and came round ... we went out. That helped a lot. The best thing that'd happened in ages — feeling really good and quite happy — but then I thought I've got to go back home again — straight back to all that shit.

SERVICES AND PROJECTS

Manchester Rape Crisis

> They were brilliant, excellent. They were there whenever I wanted them. It helped immensely to have someone there for me for the first time in my life — who didn't judge me, who didn't say I was making it all up or that I was a bloody nuisance and they'd have to limit my calls. At first when I went we just talked about everyday life. They didn't ask about the abuse. I thought 'this is great, someone just wants to talk to me about me, about my life' ... No-one tried to throw me out or rush me so I didn't feel like I needed to go out and cut myself. Pressure began to release over the nine hours I was there. Not being forced to speak. I could sit where I wanted. I could bash cushions, scream or whatever. The self-harm dwindled from three to four times a day to once a week. I didn't get sympathy — 'you poor thing' — it was great.

A Community Resource Centre

> I like it. It's more relaxed, you're treated normal. You can have a laugh. There's no nurses or shrinks and nothing gets written down — I think this place has kept me alive. It's different here because you don't feel like you're being blamed and you can leave when you want, no-one's making you come.

A general practitioner

> My doctor's good because I can go there if I'm feeling shit, instead of doing something stupid. She lets me go in a different way so I don't have to wait.

A support worker

Trust, that's what I need, people behind me, to stick by me. Just because I cut myself or end up in hospital, my support worker still treats me the same. And when I don't do anything it doesn't mean that I haven't got any problems, he still treats me the same, that's really good. It's good to be open, trust is really important . . . to listen, care, understand and agree with what I say.

EMPOWERMENT

Many young people felt that it was useful to meet other people who had been in similar situations, to share experiences and also to read or talk about how other people had survived. For some of the young people, recent literature published by Survivors Speak Out and the Bristol Crisis Service For Women, was also found to be helpful. So too was attending meetings about self-harm and attempted suicide, survivor-only groups, conferences and similar events — including the group discussions for young people run as part of this research.

It's good to be in a group because when you're on your own you're more prone to do things to yourself.

(Giving it up?) I think I would like to, but how do you find a way of doing it . . . I think that's why I want to find out about other people who have done this and how they get out of doing it.

(Reading the stuff you gave me) . . . Interestingly, it made me realise that other people do it as well and I'm not on my own. And that other people have learned to cope with it when it's been part of their lives for a long time — there's hope, if you know what I mean.

(With survivors groups) you can speak your mind and people don't talk down to you or get at you, people who've gone through the same experiences. Because usually it's professionals that have the last word. It's important that people who've done these things can get together and help each other out — and that's the best thing because you feel that you're in control . . . because we can get together and decide things.

Survivors' things, conferences, you can pick things up, understand things, there's some hope. It's good to think that you're a 'survivor', that you're surviving this, that I'm not losing, I'm winning. Because even if I cut myself and I survive that then I'm still a survivor and no-one's going to say 'God, why did you do that' and I've still got people behind me.

Only occasionally has the literature on attempted suicide and self-harm reported the importance for those involved of participating in survivors' organisations and campaigning groups. Underlying this 'absence' would seem to be the fears and misconceptions discussed earlier (Chapter 4: 'My Own Special Creation'), that mixing young people who harm themselves will result in their encouraging each other to self-harm. However, as we have already argued, such reactions generally overlook the fact that most self-harm is a very individual and private act. Engaging in 'cutting parties' or similar fantasies would work against the very purpose and meaning of the self-harm.

Indeed, it could be argued that these anxieties arise mainly out of the professionals' own fears rather than a reading of what is actually taking place. It is certainly true that some young people — when for example they are in severe distress or can see no way out of their situation or can find no alternative to harming themselves — may self-harm in front of others. However it does not follow from this that talking about it openly in a group would make their self-harming more likely. Attendance at a group would need to be optional since any offer of continuing support which was conditional on such participation could easily prove to be counter-productive.

For some young people, it is true, meeting with others who harm themselves could be threatening or frightening — for example, if they were unwilling to share or to give up their powerful individual secret. It would therefore be important to check regularly with the young person that their involvement in the group was experienced as useful. However, a young person who was finding this difficult would be likely either to stay silent or not return to the group rather than allow it to cause them to harm themselves significantly more severely. Where young people make such choices within or against a group, they should be accepted and respected.

Survivor groups can be useful in enabling young people to break out of their isolation and in countering the feelings of being bad, dirty and evil which they so often have. They can also engender powerful and potentially therapeutic feelings of solidarity and strength as well as helping to foster the development of a collective rather than an individual sense of identity.

"Helping the client find her social action niche and her political voice is an important part. If she has no sense of community with, and potential support from, others who are also beginning to face their oppressors and fight back, she may be overwhelmed by the terrors of the 'inner circle' and her symptoms are likely to recur ... Unfortunately, many therapists are still unaware of the importance of community affiliation for their self-abusive clients. There are also many therapists who insist that the reliving and reworking of the trauma in individual therapy must precede the phase of recovery in which social support and political affiliation take place." (Miller, 1994: 230)

"Having permission and space to externalise pain and anger is a powerful option. I gradually became involved with the user/survivor/self advocacy movement and made the transition from disempowered to empowered with a strong commitment to work with others for change and alternatives to conventional and dogmatic services. This movement is fighting in the same way that blacks and gays do. This is no weird concept of 'consumerism' but a social and political struggle . . . With help from my peers, I became a campaigner and trainer." (Pembroke, 1994: 37)

WHAT KIND OF SERVICES SHOULD BE PROVIDED?

A crisis service

The need which the young people identified most often was for some form of crisis service. This, they suggested, should include at least some of the following qualities and facilities:

- Directly accessible.
- Available twenty-four hours a day, seven days a week.
- Non clinical — that is, not a hospital service and not one where information is put on medical records.
- Confidential.
- Flexible so that it can take account of different needs and situations.
- Non-compulsory.
- Staffed by people who are trained in awareness and understanding of the issues facing young people who attempt suicide or self-harm, including people who themselves have been through similar experiences.

The kind of service the young people were proposing would also be able to offer:

- Medical care, where necessary.
- Rage/anger rooms *'to smash things up in'.*
- Safe/quiet rooms.
- Respect and acceptance .
- Counselling.

The service the young people had in mind was similar to that discussed in the book on self-harm written by Survivors Speak Out:

"Many of us would like to see user-led/run crisis services, where there is a phone number available to call twenty-four hours a day, seven days a week. Where someone can come to see us at a time of crisis and offer support at home or talk over the phone ... There is a clear need for self-harm helplines in every city. Many of us want access to short term sanctuary without diagnosis/ 'treatment'/drugs/sections. Houses with 'rage' facilities (a room to smash things in), where people can go without going through exhausting admission procedures." (Pembroke, 1994)

The young people generally saw this 'crisis service' as providing:

a place to go; and/or a phoneline.

Hospital Casualty/Accident and Emergency departments

The young people were clear that they should be treated with respect and dignity by hospital psychiatric wards and casualty or accident and emergency departments, including being given unconditional medical assistance without questions being asked. This is in line with the National Self-Harm Network's proposal on 'Rights for self-harmers within A&E Departments'. (See Pembroke. 1994: 56–57.)

People should be treated with respect. If they cut so bad it needs treatment, stitching, then they should be treated. But if you need to talk about it, there should be someone to listen.

Stitching — courtesy should be given unconditionally, no matter what you do, no matter how many times. But to ask 'will you have help, will you talk to somebody' and if they say 'no, get stuffed' and don't want to talk to anyone, accept it.

A non-clinical service with medical assistance

In addition, the young people talked a great deal about the need for an alternative to having to present at casualty or accident and emergency departments when they needed medical attention.

I think there should be a place, I always say that. Like instead of Casualty — another part — just for people who self-harm and stuff, so that they don't have to go through all the humiliation from staff. It doesn't have to be in hospital — but medical care if overdosing.

No shrinks or social workers — unless you wanted them. Maybe counsellors. Instead of going in and having to give your name and all that, just going in and talking if you wanted to talk to someone, so you don't have to give all your details in front of everyone at reception or shit like that.

There should be somewhere where you're allowed to go in and get medical attention e.g. getting your heart checked out, or your liver or whatever, without all the other stuff — like putting it on your records, asking loads of questions, contacting the hospital.

Something, somewhere not attached to anything, that didn't even take your name or anything, where you could go and get checked out, and if you had done something they could give you something just to make it better.

Damage limitation

It was important for the young people that services did not have a policy which in effect denied them help simply on the grounds that they had attempted suicide or had self-harmed. Indeed, even if their self-harming took place actually on the premises of a hospital or helping agency, they were not necessarily prepared to accept that attempts should be made to stop them. If a service was not prepared to operate on such a principle, many of the young people indicated that they would not use it. If they did carry on attending, they might well not tell anyone there about their self-harm, or they might find somewhere else to self-harm after they had left the agency.

In fact, what the young people were looking for was a facility — especially in relation to self-harm such as cutting — which would offer a range of safety measures to limit the damage. These might include someone to whom they could talk either before or after they had self-harmed, safety kits and medical assistance (or at least a second opinion) if they thought this was necessary.

To care physically for you no matter what time of day, to say 'come down and we can talk and see if it makes a difference and if after an hour or so it doesn't then there's still somewhere you can go and cut — a room if you've got to'. Bandages, antiseptic, someone to treat it if necessary and not treat you like a leper and say that you're a pile of shit because you've just come here, you've used us and then you've gone off and done it anyway. They might still want to do that for the first few times but after a while it might diffuse it as long as they've still got that option there that they can still do that.

People would still go outside and do it if they weren't allowed to in there. A small room with a medical kit. Because once they've cut and the tension is relieved they might be able to come out and talk then. Rather than 'piss off, you've done it now, you've been here two hours'. Then after a while people would think of going down and talking more before they cut the next time. Changing the order you do things. That would have helped me.

If someone felt that they were going to cut themselves really badly they could phone up and come down there and do it in a room with a medical kit and confidentiality. Come and talk and someone to talk to afterwards rather than saying don't do it. Somewhere safe for people. Counselling as well.

Thus, for many of the young people it was very important that, when they were using a service, their multi-purpose coping mechanism was not taken away from them or prohibited. Clearly, this raises complicated issues for services. From the young people's point of view, however, it was crucial to be able to hold on to this part of themselves, at least to the extent of knowing that their self-harming *'is there if I need it'*.

> *A place to go where you've got an option whether you do it or not, like a house. It'd be useful if there were people there who'd been through it as well, people properly trained and who understand.*

> *I think I would have gone somewhere like that if it was confidential and I knew there would have been someone there to listen, not necessarily to stop me.*

> *The big thing for me was hating feeling processed. I don't think you could have somewhere without it having some structure though. It's a difficult compromise between complete freedom and not having control taken away from you and having some control over your own life, because although people think self-harm is about being out of control it's something very in control that you do because it puts you in control. When you're doing it you're in control of yourself. So then to take it all away from you, I think that's why you want to do it again because everything you've just spent hours building up has just been taken away.*

Non-compulsory

Such suggestions were linked into the young people's more general ideas about the non-compulsory nature of services they would like to see. They recognised the problems and risks associated with attempted suicide and self-harm and the sense of responsibility felt by the services and the professionals working for them. Nonetheless, they saw it as important that they should not feel pushed or coerced into receiving certain forms of help or treatment or to attend a particular service.

> *A crisis service, if you could just go there until you felt all right . . . as long as you could leave when you wanted to leave. But then I'm not sure if there was a place like that whether they would let you leave, because if it was like that I wouldn't go . . . but if I knew of a place that was open all those times when I felt absolutely shit and I was going to do something and I sort of wanted to stop myself but I didn't really have the control to, if I could get myself to a place like that until those feelings went away, then that would be all right . . . but you can't just go to the hospital because you'd never get out.*

User control

This last quotation reiterates what this report has highlighted many times: how issues of control are fundamental to the young person's need for and experience of their self-harm.

Where this is the case services, forms of support and approaches to individual young people are needed which work with and which do not undermine, this sense of being in control. Again this is discussed specifically in some recent work on women and self-harm.

"The last thing our self-mutilating sister needs is someone to take away her one area of control. We assist rather by respecting this need for control, by not interfering with the expression it takes, and by co-exploring the reality and the difficulty that powerlessness poses. We can assist as well by helping her gain more power in the world and feel entitled to that power. Women who exercise power in the world in which they live and who feel entitled to do so do not need to mutilate or over-control their bodies. And we assist by politicizing control itself." (Burstow, 1992: 196)

Earlier studies have emphasised too that, in order to minimise the incidence of self-harm, it is important that service initiatives have an open-door policy. They need also to avoid leaving the young people feeling coerced into changing their behaviour by forms of treatment imposed on them by professionals. Their approaches therefore need to be based on respect for the young people and need to assume that the young people have responsibility for what may happen. Those who self-harm can then feel that they have some control over their treatment or care; that this is their own; and that they are responsible for making changes in their behaviour. (See for example Crabtree and Grossman, 1974; Ross and McKay, 1979.)

As the recent report by the Bristol Crisis Service for Women emphasises:

"Taking self injury and what lies behind it may be something a woman does in her own way, in partnership with different sorts of helpers, rather than something which is done to her by means of 'treatment' prescribed by others". (Arnold, 1995: 23)

Let people hang on to the control that they've already took by whatever means (self-harm if they want).

I don't think psychiatry's the answer, they should treat people who self-harm decently and listen to them and try to understand and find out what you want to happen, what you think would help, not what they want and what they think would help.

Somewhere very non-condemnatory. Somewhere very 'right you can do — what would you like to do?' Very much leaving the choice in the individuals' own hands.

I think I'd have liked kind of a 'second opinion' to look at the injury without shock and tell me if they thought it needed medical attention and if it did then give me the option of what I wanted to do about it — 'yes it does, let me take you there' or instead 'no it doesn't but if you want to go I'll still go with you' sort of thing. But then again, I know it's difficult on the other side. It's all very well me saying give people all the control they want but if someone's going to die or whatever . . .

Rage rooms/rooms to smash things up in

What would have helped at that time would have been being allowed to go into a room and scream and shout as much as I wanted. When I was in hospital, other people were like that so they came up on the idea that it would be a good idea to have a padded room. Nothing was done about it. The staff just think we were all mad you see.

A place to go, run by women. People in touch with young people. Take who you want with you. A room with a great big pit full of balls, things you can smash but you bounce in and kick and scream — can't hurt yourself with — bounce against the wall, play room. Paints and things. Twenty-four hours.

There would have to be a few staff there. Where you couldn't harm yourself or anyone else. Kick and scream, shout. And when you've had enough you could sit down and talk about how you feel — like if you want to self-harm to talk about what it feels like.

I always wanted to be able to be put in a padded room to be able to smash everything up — to break something — I would have got great pleasure in being able to put a brick through a window and watching it crumble but I never would because I was always brought up to not do stuff like that.

I think that's a really good idea because if you do it in your own room then you break something and have to pay for it (and you feel bad after). I always wanted a punching bag or you'd do it to yourself — its harmful. I love getting a bat and hitting it against the wall to get it all out — and feel much better, make a load of noise.

I smash things up in my room, it feels good at the time but you feel worse after. (A room to smash things up in?) that's a good idea, as long as you still don't get judged by it. As long as no-one was watching I'd be fine.

Flexibility

It was important for many of the young people that the support and care they received was not rigid and did not pigeon-hole them. Services were seen as needing to respond to individuals by taking account of different needs — both of different people and of the same person at different times. The range of functions which self-harm has for the young people at different times highlights this. Responses based on pre-set ideas and assumptions about what self-harm or attempted suicide means for an individual are unlikely to be helpful and certainly do not provide a basis for deciding what interventions to make.

The young people thus emphasised the importance of services being flexible in the kinds of support they offered to them. Some of them for example wanted somewhere where they could hand over their pills (though not have them taken away from them) and then stay for a few hours until the feelings they were dealing with had subsided. Many of them would have liked the option, not only of being able to talk to someone, but also of having somewhere safe to go where they would not be expected to talk to anyone unless they chose to do so. One young woman would have liked a night 'retreat' for times when she felt she might harm herself, though without <u>having</u> to stay.

Many of the young people also stressed the importance of a facility to which they could go <u>before</u> they felt like harming themselves, so they would not *'get to feel like that'*. However here too the need for variety and flexibility in service provision was highlighted since some of them acknowledged that, even if this was available, they still might not use it. For a few of them, going to such a centre or service when they felt they were going to harm themselves would

change the reason why I wanted to cut up or attempt suicide in the first place.

What some of the young people seemed to be saying, in fact, was: *'if I really wanted to do it why would I go?'* These reactions were often related to a fear of being seen as manipulative as well as to feelings of shame and embarrassment about what they did to themselves. Here again therefore — this time in the context of service provision and in particular their need to talk to someone — we can see the importance of not reinforcing a young person's anxieties by referring to them as attention-seeking.

The evidence suggests that those young people who at a particular time might feel they want to harm themselves but would want to find a way of not doing so might be more inclined to use a 'place-to-go' kind of facility if it were on offer. However, there are also likely to be young people who at any moment do not want to stop their self-harming and who may be unable or unwilling to seek such support or sanctuary. A need therefore seems to exist for a service for both groups.

This is <u>not</u> to suggest that those being targeted comprise two types of young person; the same individual could well be in either situation at different times. Indeed, it is more likely that they will experience considerable ambivalence as they struggle with both sets of feelings simultaneously. However, where the desire or need to self-harm overrides the desire not to self-harm, then the evidence suggests that it is not helpful for the young people to go somewhere where the emphasis is on <u>not</u> doing it. This could mean that they may end up not using the facility and so not receive any support at all.

It is possible that, if a different kind of service — a 'place to go' — were offered along the lines outlined here, it would be more accessible to those young people who at present have doubts about whether they would use it. It would need to provide forms of support which do not make stopping self-harming <u>an expectation</u>, which do not imply that the young people or the service providers have failed if the self-harming does not stop, and which do not punish or judge the young people if they continue to harm themselves. Such facilities might then be attractive and accessible enough to enable those young people, who do not feel able to make a commitment to stop self-harming, to use them.

We cannot just expect many young people who harm themselves simply to present themselves voluntarily to a service for support in the confidence that once there they will receive the support they feel they need.

> *If I wanted to stop I may need support... I think quite a lot of things would help but I don't think it's as simple as someone saying 'come in to this great new project' — it's just not as simple as that.*

(For a more in-depth discussion of these issues see the next chapter — *'It's Like Two Thoughts Going On').*

Phoneline

One possible solution to some of these difficulties could be the provision of a phoneline. The young people who talked about the problems of going somewhere for support felt that they might use a phoneline because it would be anonymous. A key condition however was that it should be staffed by people who responded in certain appropriate ways.

> *A phoneline is a good idea. Run by women — people who have either gone through it themselves or people who won't judge, who believe you. Learn lessons from Rape Crisis — believe what women say. Open twenty-four hours a day.*

> *There should be a suicide line/phone line or something, or a place you can go, twenty-four hours, seven days a week, to be able to talk about it.*

What sort of attitudes would be useful at a crisis centre or phoneline?

In order to clarify how provision might be improved, we need to remind ourselves of the picture painted in the previous chapter ('Not A Clue') of the <u>unhelpful</u> responses which the young people had experienced and in particular their frequently reiterated view that they had never received a positive or helpful response to their suicide attempts or their self-harm.

However, as we also saw, this did not mean that they believed that no positive responses were possible. What seemed to be extremely important for achieving these — as the recent study by the Bristol Crisis Service for Women (Arnold, 1995) also concluded — were the attitudes and approaches of individual workers.

Trust and tender loving care

In the group discussions the young people emphasised the importance of establishing trust with the people who were supporting them. Some felt strongly that, though this trust was essential, it was fragile and was all too often lost or broken. This could happen because, for example, of 'grassing'; because their GP was told about their attempted suicide or self-harming; or by being sent to hospital or being discharged or moved on when the young person had cut-up. For some of the young people in the group discussions *once trust is lost or broken — that's it.*

The young people also emphasised the importance of staff being honest and *'up front'* and of feeling that the staff cared about them.

As well as wanting somewhere safe to vent their anger and frustration, some of the young people were also looking for the warmth and safety of physical and nurturing responses, contact and security. Clearly this would need to be offered sensitively and would need to be negotiated and checked with the young person.

> *You need the anger side and the safety side — both sides.*

> *To give me a cuddle if I needed it. 'Do you want me to put my arms round you and hold you?' That is a way of diffusing tension sometimes because you think no-one wants to come near you because you're disgusting/dirty/ worthless.*

> *What would help would be the opposite of what I've got. Instead of saying nasty things — love, cuddling, a positive response.*

> *I would like a place, probably a man who would give me a hug just to wrap me up and that's it, somewhere where you could talk. No time limit, someone you can cuddle up to and cry on. You can't do that with social workers — they're patronising.*

Respect and acceptance

One young man, by suggesting that this report should be called *Accepting the Unacceptable* vividly illustrated the importance for people who self-harm of being given respect and acceptance. This same demand is currently being strongly articulated by the emerging movement on self-harm — the Self-harm Network.

> "I am not suggesting professionals should merely show us kindness. I am saying that there needs to be some respect, and self-harm is seen as a valid expression of distress." (Pembroke, 1994: 45)

The young people in this study talked too about the importance of staff and services recognising and accepting a young person's behaviour so they do not feel judged or criticised.

> *A recognition that it's your way of coping even though they might not agree with it.*

> *That they wouldn't ask questions, unless you want to speak to them obviously. To just say things like 'you're feeling shit and it doesn't matter that you're feeling shit and it doesn't really matter why you're feeling shit' but that they can accept the fact that you are feeling like that ... Not to suggest that you've got no <u>right</u> to feel shit and that there's other people out there who are worse off than you because I know that but it doesn't stop you feeling shit. That's the last thing you need to hear because it makes you feel even more guilty.*

To accept that some people do that and they shouldn't have to know the reason why . . . Not to make them feel as guilty as hell when they have done it.

For many of the young people, part of this process involved being given the opportunity or permission to say they had self-harmed and/or were continuing to harm themselves without feeling that this was wrong or that they should have stopped.

(It would have helped) if they'd have said 'we know what might be going on for you and if you're self-harming, cutting, attempting suicide, it's not going to affect how we feel about you and you can tell us, or you don't have to.'

Keep the channels open — not closing things off and not trying to cheer you up. Making it okay to say you're still doing it. Someone to talk to about what you feel like. Acknowledging that it is happening and that it's kind of positive. Someone who didn't mind talking about it and maybe even asking about it — not probing but making it okay to talk and recognising that it's done good things for you in the past even if you wanted to stop. Just being open and not being scared.

Such an approach is in line with some of the guidelines set out by Burstow in relation to working with women who self-harm.

"It is easier for the client to accept herself and to trust us if we make it clear that we accept and respect her just as she is . . . make it clear that you understand that self mutilation has served her well and that you have no intention of robbing her of it." (Burstow, 1992: 191–4)

This again would seem to involve recognising the many functions which attempted suicide and self-harm play in a young person's life. Many of the young people thought it important that other people accepted their behaviour. Again, this did not necessarily mean ignoring it but it did mean recognising the distress it caused and (as outlined above) finding strategies of 'damage and risk-limitation'. During one of the group discussions, for example, the young people talked about the possibilities of workers or carers responding positively by conveying the message that: *'It's good that you've found this; but what about considering ways of looking after yourself'.*

Developing informed choices

As we saw earlier in this chapter, the young people often expressed ambivalence about whether they were able to or wanted to stop harming themselves. (For more in-depth discussion of this, see also Chapter 3: 'A Clock Ticking' and Chapter 8: 'It's Like Two Thoughts Going On'.) Some of them felt that it would be helpful to have more information available to them so that they could become more knowledgeable about self-harm and make more informed decisions on their own self-harming. For some this might involve thinking about continuing, reducing or stopping self-harming, or about whether to look at underlying issues.

I wasted a lot of time and I think I wasn't ready but I'm convinced there must have been a way of making me ready — for me to have been able to make an informed choice. I don't know what the way is but I can't help thinking it because otherwise you could go through and always not be ready . . . I didn't feel like I knew what it was, or what my options were.

These increased forms of information and understanding could enable the development of approaches which are in line with those they outlined earlier for negotiating acceptance, honesty and trust between themselves and whoever may be supporting them and keeping the channels of communication open. They might also involve providing information and educative material on self-harm for workers.

To ask about it

For the development of more informed choices, it would seem important that professionals ask the young people about their self-harming. However, this could be a very delicate process. As we have seen, the young people often felt intimidated and lectured at by professionals who asked why they self-harm in ways which seemed to assume that it could be explained simply and in a few minutes. For many young people sensitive questioning without probing would be needed to provide an important way in to their distress.

Although I do think it was a symptom, it would have helped to talk about it. As it was I just did it more because if you don't concentrate on that, it could be anything that's upsetting you and you could go round everything to see what it is.

One young woman suggested that staff who were asking about situations in which the young people might feel like self-harming again might use questions and comments like:

'What does it feel like?' 'What's in your head now?' 'How bad is the pressure?' and 'Sit there for a while and see if it gets any worse — and talk about anything you want'.

The young people frequently made it clear that just being able to talk about their self-harm would not necessarily mean that they would no longer need to do it — that, again, it *'wasn't that simple'.* However, if they were not once more to be made to feel bad or guilty about their behaviour, it was important that this should not be seen as a failure either by the young person or the staff. Nor did it mean that talking about it made it worse: this would depend on <u>how</u> it was talked about. Many of the young people resented having attention drawn to their self-harm in ways which meant that other people made a fuss about it and over-reacted.

Linked to this too was a view held by some of the young people that, whether they had harmed themselves or not, they should not be treated any differently.

If you approach someone about it you should be treated the same whether you've done it or not, that's what doesn't happen.

As with many of the issues raised here, this was expressed particularly clearly in relation to self-harm without suicidal intent: it may not have applied in the same way to life threatening situations like a suicide attempt or to self-harm 'gone wrong' where medical attention was clearly required.

We have already seen how many of the therapeutic approaches used in response to self-harm were based on behaviourist assumptions about deliberate self-harm being a learnt maladaptive behaviour which can be unlearnt. Within such approaches, the form of attention given (or not given) by the staff to the behaviour was then seen as crucial. As far as the young people were concerned however this did not appear to be the main issue. What mattered to many of them was not whether they were given more or less attention when they harmed themselves but whether they received some consistency of care. They wanted to feel that they were being seen as a whole person rather than simply being defined in terms of their self-harm.

They also were looking for some recognition that, though their <u>not</u> having self-harmed for a while <u>may</u> be a progressive step for them, it need not necessarily be so. This kind of judgement, it seemed, could reflect the individual worker's need and wish for the young person to stop their self-harming or their own need to feel that they were succeeding. It need not reflect what the young person required, which would depend largely on their individual needs and the specific nature and context of their self-harm.

These personal circumstances also included whether or not the young person was feeling pressurised — by professionals, family, friends, themselves, work, college or anyone else — not to harm themselves. After all, a young person's difficulties could still be very real for them and, even though they may not have harmed themselves for some time, no less acute. As we have also argued many times, if the young person suppresses the urge or desire to self-harm, the consequence for them the next time could be that they harm themselves even more seriously.

I need people behind me, supporting me, and at times having a safe environment and I need to be treated like anyone else, not like a mad person. Because I'm not mad. I've just got problems due to the past and my coping mechanisms aren't very good.

CHAPTER 8

'It's Like Two Thoughts Going On'

Conflict and Dilemmas for young people

This chapter examines some of the conflicts and paradoxes embedded in the young people's understandings of their behaviour. It begins by presenting the researcher's own perceptions of these dilemmas, before going on to consider in more detail some of the ways in which young people who repeatedly self-harm describe these for themselves.

Conflicts and paradoxes — the nub of the problem for young people — and helpers.

This study's considerable evidence on young people's strongly conflicting feelings about and reactions to their own behaviour clearly poses some very difficult dilemmas for professionals and other helpers. Indeed, if taken simply at its generalised level, it could be seen as suggesting that whatever they do is likely to be wrong, inappropriate, unhelpful. Thus some of the most important messages conveyed by the young people through the research could be reduced to statements like:

- I want someone to listen but I can't tell anyone.
- I want to talk about it but it's all about not being able to say anything and about there being no words for it — it's beyond words or understanding.
- I want attention but I'm not worthy of it.
- I want to stop but it feels good and I'm not sure what I'd be left with.
- I want people to notice and care but I hide it .
- It's O.K. for me to do it to myself but it's not O.K. for others — they shouldn't have to.
- I deserve it and they don't.
- It feels like it's to do with control but it also feels it's not control because I need to do it.
- This is a way in which I don't have to think about difficult things, therefore talking about it will mean I'll have to think about it and that's not what I want.

- If I do it I'll feel better; if I do it I'll feel worse.

- It's mine so people shouldn't interfere with it but sometimes it scares me and I can't handle it — I might go too far. But then again I want to go too far because that's what it's all about.

- I want to approach people, ask for help, but that's a really hard thing to do and I can't guarantee it'll help.

- Harming myself might make me feel worse but at least I know what I'll get from it — it works.

For those wishing to offer help or support to young people who self-harm, the main conclusion to be drawn from this would seem to be that as far as possible, before any decisive intervention is attempted, every individual young person's starting point and situation needs to be individualised. This means that it would have to be 'read' as carefully and incisively as possible, the (often inherently contradictory) contents of this reading respected and weighed and a judgement made on where the balances of the young person's feelings and expectations seemed to be falling. A tentative response or responses might then be made based on these kinds of interpretations rather than on preconceptions about the young person as a 'self-harmer' or 'an attempted suicide' or on a doctrinaire commitment to certain kinds of intervention strategies.

Language/communication

(Communication?) Yes but not necessarily to other people but just expressing what is there. It's like a word that isn't a word.

Suicide and self-harm, it has often been suggested, need to be understood as veiled strategies for communicating with others. Yet, as we have seen, most of the time the young people in this study behaved as they did for the immediate effects they could have on themselves and not simply in order to adopt a perverse or pathological communication strategy. It seems likely that suicide or self-harm which is attempted only once or twice may contain this element of communication. However, its 'repetition' would appear to have more to do with the intrapersonal functions it serves than with acting as a form of direct, or even indirect, communication designed to have an impact on others.

Indeed, for many of the young people their behaviour represented something which they felt was beyond words — for which there were *'no words to express how I'm feeling'*.

I don't think it's something that can be put into words. There are only so many words.

For some individuals, this reaction could occur because expressing their feelings in words would be too painful — because it would stir up overwhelming thoughts, emotions and memories. One young woman reflected on her conflict and difficulties when talking about such painful experiences.

I think it's because you can't say anything that you do it, because I can't say anything. But then it doesn't help to say anything anyway, it doesn't really communicate anything either. Well maybe it tells somebody that you're unhappy but that doesn't serve any purpose ... but I think I'd be dead if I hadn't told anybody but it still doesn't make the feelings go away.

Difficulties about talking were often reinforced by interventions which simply asked a young person why they did it and whether or not there was suicidal intent.

I've been in Casualty with my wrists slashed or I've taken an overdose and people ask me what's the matter and I just can't put it into words.

I get like that now if I'm having a bad time and people ask me what's wrong. I say 'Nothing, I'm fine' and that's the way I work because I can't put things into words when I'm like that. I just can't do it.

Something on the inside trying to get on the outside

Not a language, no, or a way of communicating, well I suppose it is in a way — something on the inside trying to get outside — trying to work something out — that can't be talked about. Maybe it's a way of communicating the feelings that you can't express.

A hidden or confused need for contact and communication was sometimes expressed by the young person. As Miller (1994: 45) makes clear in "Women Who Hurt Themselves", though an individual may find numerous ways of asking others for help through their self-harm, she is at the same time

"always ambivalent and is simultaneously finding ways to distance herself from the very people she cries out to."

Miller goes on to describe the self-protective function which the behaviour provides which will "keep others at a distance".

The pulls and the pushes

Strong feelings — both 'push' and 'pull' — thus exist within an individual and their environment in relation to talking to someone, being listened to, and getting help or support. Thus pushes away from or pulls towards getting help can be experienced simultaneously. Experiences of abuse often produce the strongest 'push' element in order to hide the distress or fear of not being believed, of being punished and so on.

Then (at the start) I think it was for attention to be honest. I wanted someone to help me, like a cry for help because things were going wrong ... my step-dad was beating me up all the time and I was being abused. I couldn't trust anyone, I just wanted someone to listen.

Q — Did you get attention?

No because no-one really knew about it because I hid it. I couldn't trust anyone in my own family — I couldn't tell them about the abuse... All I wanted was someone to listen, to be taken away from the situation, someone to notice without me having to tell them.

You need attention — there's something drastically wrong but you can't actually say to anyone ' look I need your help' so you tell in another way.

Q — About saying — 'look what's happening to me'?

I suppose it was in a way because I can't see a reason why I did it otherwise.

The taboos, embarrassment and shame around the behaviour and the emotions associated with it may also be a barrier to communication. The following quotation demonstrates the problem arising from attitudes which see self-harm as manipulative and the way these can reinforce a young person's ambivalent feelings about themselves.

I think I probably was communicating but then when I did (tell someone) I just regretted it so much. The first time I told anyone I felt so stupid. I felt like I was being manipulative. If I was doing it for myself why would I tell anyone.

The importance of the behaviour belonging to, and being controlled by, the young person could thus co-exist with a need or desire to communicate and be understood. The group discussions particularly highlighted the dilemmas that young people may face. On the one hand they often sought shared experience and commonality with others and wanted to be understood and even to be helped. On the other, a very strong individualistic element existed within their behaviour which defined it as *'mine'* and which worked against their wanting others to know about it, or *'get in on it'*.

This promoted the privacy and secrecy around the behaviour which, as we have seen, could be a source of strength for the individual. Talking or getting help could be extremely threatening for a young person where they felt they risked exposure. They might also wonder whether the behaviour would be taken away from them once it was known about — and what then would they be left with? The fear here seemed to be that what they would be left with were all the feelings, the trauma, the memories and so on which the behaviour may have disguised or in some ways held in check.

It is important to recognise these 'pushes' away from talking and seeking help, and that they were present for a reason and at times could provide a young person with a powerful means of dealing with difficult experiences and emotions. They also suggest that responses to the behaviour could not be as simple as just seeking to replace the 'pushes' with the 'pulls' as this would miss some of the positive aspects of self-harming for the young person.

Indeed, the range of 'pushes' and 'pulls' need to be examined in more detail if we are to understand them and how they might manifest themselves.

On the one hand, the young people displayed their wish to keep their behaviour for themselves in a variety of ways.

Doing something to myself, for myself.

It's not for other people, it's for yourself (myself).

It's yours so they shouldn't interfere, they interfere because they don't see it as normal.

Isn't as simple as this. It's all about not being defined. In a way we wouldn't want people to understand.

At the same time the young people often acknowledged that such feelings and thoughts could at times become a barrier to seeking the support they may need.

I felt like I'd done it for me, therefore there was no point in talking about it because I was doing it for me and it was only a symptom anyway so I didn't need to discuss it. I thought it would be a waste of time talking about it and also because it was just really embarrassing.

I think if people are still doing it then there's a reason why they're still doing it — that is, they hate themselves, they don't believe they deserve to have a nice life, to talk to somebody. I used to think that I didn't want to talk to anyone else about it. It wasn't anyone's business, it's got nothing to do with anyone else. But when I did I just felt that somebody was actually prepared to listen to how I feel and why.

You've got to want to be able to do it — have the support of as many people as possible and bring it out in the open, not hide it from people.

The conflict expressed by many of the young people between on the one hand seeking support and understanding and on the other wanting the behaviour to belong to them could mean that frequently an individual would not go anywhere for help. If a young person felt that the self-harming was something they were doing for themselves, going somewhere or approaching someone about it could seem like betraying themselves in some way — that is, that perhaps after all they did not <u>really</u> want or need to harm themselves, otherwise why would they want to tell someone?

Q — Somewhere to go?

It would change the reason why I wanted to cut up or commit suicide in the first place.

Q — Would you have gone somewhere?

I don't know. I have to say that it's all such a personal and private thing that I don't think I would have ... I wouldn't personally have wanted to go anywhere when I felt like that because I would have thought that I couldn't have really wanted to do it otherwise I wouldn't go. Because before I would have thought if I go saying I feel like it, I obviously don't feel like it <u>enough</u> otherwise I would just do it. Because if I wanted to do it why would I go, and if I did go I would feel like I was being manipulative. So then I would just do it anyway because that's what I wanted to do. If I did go then I'd think that if I'd wanted to do it why would I have gone so I'd do it anyway and afterwards I'd feel so stupid, so guilty.

The act of self-harm, the functions it serves and the meanings it has for the young person can thus <u>in themselves</u> become a barrier to getting help or support. They can act as a very strong defence mechanism.

Cutting became normal because I did it so much so it helped me think that everything was all right.

Problems with approaching people

For some young people it was so hard to seek help that often, rather than do this, they would hurt themselves. There could be a variety of reasons why they found it more helpful to self-harm in addition to the felt need to keep the behaviour for themselves. These could include its immediate benefits (for example, providing relief), the stigma and prejudice surrounding the behaviour, their not knowing what response they may get and their feeling that they do not deserve or need attention or support.

It's so difficult to keep approaching people. I can only do it so many times before I have to cut myself because I know I'm helping myself by doing that, I'm getting something out of it. I know it sounds daft but I don't feel I'm getting something out of it by approaching people because I'm avoiding it. Because you're preventing it, it's still there, you still want to do it, it just holds it for so long, it's like it's on 'pause'.

A lot of people who self-harm would prefer to do it than approach people about it because it's more difficult to approach someone saying you're going to cut yourself, it's easier to do it. People don't realise how difficult it is for me to say 'Look I feel like doing it'. It's more helpful just to do it.

The young people also expressed some conflicting views on the responses and reactions they thought they needed or wanted which again illustrated the perplexing situations often faced by helpers and the need, as suggested at the start of this chapter, for as careful a 'reading' as can be achieved of the young person's situation. These conflicts included, for example, the young people wanting their behaviour both to be ignored and also to be noticed, asked and talked about.

I hate it when someone asks me about it. I prefer if they didn't mention it.

Q — Would you want people to care that you've hurt yourself?
No, because to me it's an everyday thing now.

Q — How do you want people to react?
Just be normal. Ignore it. They used to leave me alone and it was great. I could do what I liked and they didn't pester me.

It was kind of ignored, and I wanted it ignored but I don't know whether I really wanted it ignored.

I used to lie to nurse — 'Do you feel all right?' 'Yes, thank you very much'. He never challenged me, 'Is that true?' Maybe I would have opened up more. I didn't want to stop anyway. I was only going because of them.

It could also be that some individuals deny to others and to themselves that they are worried about their behaviour.

I also lied when I said it wasn't a big deal when it was.

This again could embody another conflict for them — that 'I care about myself and I want to survive but I don't give a shit about myself and I deserve to be hurt or to die'. This could manifest itself in continual confusion and battles within a young person over whether or not to harm themselves and whether or not to stop.

To me it feels awful because it's about control but is it control when I cut up or when I don't cut up . . . It's like two thoughts going on — cut up or not and it's what gains you most strength out of it.

For the first few months it was everyday . . . I did it seriously for about six months and then pretty regular — about once a week and I thought about killing myself a few times and then it kind of faded away and it got to the point where I wanted to do it but I didn't want to do it.

I really don't think about giving it up.

Q — Do you want to get to the bottom of it?
Sometimes I do. When I'm on a really good day I think I'll go out and get things solved, get a job, but when I'm having a totally shitty day I just don't give a fuck.

Q — Do you want to stop?

I don't know. Sometimes I do and sometimes I don't.

A further conflict which a young person might express focussed on whether harming themselves was an *'O.K. thing to do'.* Whilst they might feel it was right and proper for them to do it, they also frequently expressed concerns about other people who hurt themselves.

> *I don't like it when other people do it. (Me and Chris) have lots of arguments over it because I don't think it's right that she does it, but it's all right for me and she feels the same as well. We're close now and you don't like seeing someone else doing it. Well, I don't anyway.*

Many of the young people often expressed great insight into the responsibilities and difficulties workers face in situations where a young person might be harming themselves or attempting suicide. A young person might often feel conflict and confusion over whether they wanted to be helped or left to control their own destiny. In such circumstances an individual might want to be in control of their behaviour while at times recognising that their life could be at risk.

> *But then again, I know it's difficult on the other side. It's all very well me saying give people all the control they want, but if someone's going to die, or whatever.*

Sometimes these conflicts and ambiguities could be felt so strongly that the young person could feel overwhelmed and trapped by the extreme nature of the opposing emotions. In these reactions we can again see how in some ways self-harm itself could be used to deal with what may seem like an unbearable and untenable position. At the risk of over-generalising, it might even be possible to say that self-harm is the expression of and temporary relief from overwhelming, unbearable and often conflicting emotions and feelings.

Some interventions, it would seem, can reinforce that part of a young person's feelings or consciousness which denies their wish or need for help. If these conflicts do exist for an individual, then responses which see the behaviour as attention-seeking may drive them even further away from any support. In addition, many of the other interventions and reactions which the young people identified in this study as problematic — for example, being 'moved on', not being believed, being punished when asking for help — might have a similar effect.

CHAPTER 9

Who's Hurting Who?

Concluding Comments

Whose definitions count?

This research has attempted to articulate the views and feelings of some young people who have repeatedly attempted suicide and/or harmed themselves. As we have seen, these young people were frequently socially and emotionally marginalised. As with many marginalised sections of society, they were usually effectively silenced — denied access and opportunities to contribute to debates on the meaning and treatment of their behaviour.

Far from their behaviour being meaningless or nonsensical, the young people offered complex understandings of it and rationales for its continuation, including some explanations of why so often they hold onto it so strongly. The insights emerging from the research will therefore, it is hoped, do two things: illuminate what may be required to redress the balance of power and knowledge in favour of those who are most directly affected by the experiences of self-harm and attempted suicide; and actually contribute something to this process.

By attempting to gather together the meanings and understandings expressed by the young people — that is, by presenting their accounts of their behaviour — this research will hopefully add something to the struggle currently going on to legitimise such self-presentations. What is more, as a research document which may be in a relatively powerful position to make such statements, it is also intended as an addition to a slowly growing body of literature and related campaigning activities around self-harm. These are now emanating for example from the Self-harm Network and the Bristol Crisis Service for Women. How much power and legitimacy these accounts will have for changing attitudes, interventions and policies of course remains to be seen.

Echoes exist within this piece of research, too, of other, more general debates and struggles over mental health issues and the control of the meanings, definitions and acceptability of certain behaviours and emotions. During the group discussions the young people constantly reflected about, and questioned others' judgements on the appropriateness of their behaviour, sometimes actually asserting: *'it seems rational — the right thing to do.'* These discussions thus explored whether and how far certain behaviours seen as unintelligible by the observer may for the individual concerned be a 'sane response to an intolerable situation'.

At such moments they therefore evoked familiar 'Laingian' themes — older arguments developed in the work of for example Laing (1965), Cooper (1970) and others. It seems important to restate that the young people were often clearly ambivalent about their behaviour and were clearly not saying in any straightforward way that they saw or experienced their self-harm as a better way of being.

More recently, the Hearing Voices Network (see Romme and Escher, 1993) has exemplified a similar struggle to establish the acceptability and validity of experiences and responses labelled as 'deviant'. Similarly — and in line with the aims of the National Self-harm Network — the young people in this study were often asking for recognition and acceptance of their behaviour as a valid way of expressing their distress.

These two particular struggles have at least one common focus: the need to explore the relevant behaviours and experiences rather than deny their existence or try to prevent them from happening. Above all this means acknowledging that these behaviours and experiences have meaning. This research also points to the need to accept and recognise such meanings. It is clear that the contentious debates and negotiations on the definitions of 'sanity', 'madness' and 'appropriate behaviour' which are taking place at a 'macro' level are constantly reproduced in more 'micro' arenas. These include research studies such as this (for example, during its interviews and group discussions) and on a day-to-day basis within a young person's interaction with professionals, helpers and carers.

Findings — what findings?

Within this relatively neglected area of theory and of practice, it is not possible to offer any simple answers or solutions. Indeed, this study is clearly limited in its ability to provide insights into whether a certain hypothesis on causation is 'true' or whether certain interventions 'work'. This was never its intention. Nor, since it was never meant to be a 'number crunching' exercise, has it been able to offer generalised statistics or assertions.

Its rationale, and hopefully the importance of its 'results', lie in its attempt to develop authentic in-depth accounts of self-harm and attempted suicide as constructed by young people themselves — as far as possible to give voice to their insights and meanings. However, precisely because many of these pose a range of conflicts and dilemmas for both the young people themselves and their carers, the research has not pointed to any clear conclusions or recommendations. More importantly, it has raised questions — such as:

- How far are services, workers and carers aware of these insights and meanings as defined by the young people?
- How far are services, workers and carers prepared to take them seriously?

- What are they prepared (or able) to do with them?
- What implications do these insights have for training and supporting workers?

What such questions do make clear, however, is that the research has raised issues which go beyond the clinical assessment and management of self-harm and attempted suicide. In addition, it has pointed to other questions concerned with reactions to and meanings of such behaviour — and indeed, beyond this again, to a need to question the role and impact of many of the clinical approaches themselves.

As we saw in the last chapter, young people who repeatedly attempt suicide or self-harm are often only too aware of the dilemmas associated with their behaviour and are to some degree able and willing to share these. This report has tried to express and clarify some of these difficulties, ambiguities and complexities and to highlight the many conflicts these experiences pose for workers, services and young people themselves.

These 'research findings' have thus not been easy to grasp and write up: indeed in a conventional sense they perhaps ought not to be labelled as such! All that the study has identified is contained within the previous pages of this report which cannot therefore be easily concluded or summarised. It has tried to be as open as possible about the range of differences, conflicts and complexities which have been illuminated by the research and to cover the multitude of meanings and understandings, including their many pros and cons, offered by the young people. As far as possible this variety of meanings and the richness of the material have not been suppressed in order to make the report easier or clearer to write (or read).

Treatment, control and the experience of hurt

Insofar as the report does have as a conclusion, it re-emphasises some of the key issues embedded in the theme 'Who's hurting who?', including some of the dilemmas facing services and workers.

One of the issues which has arisen centrally throughout the research concerns the struggle over control: both of self-harm itself and of its meaning: Who controls the hurt? Who owns the behaviour? What does it mean?

> "Speaking metaphorically, when the Doctor shocks John for striking himself or banging his head, he may be confusing John as to who is the mutilator — John or the doctor. Who is punishing whom? The doctor seems to be taking over control of John's self-injurious behaviour — it is no longer his behaviour; no longer a proprietary act; it is behaviour which is now controlled by others; John's self-injurious behaviour has been co-opted. Similarly it may be that when Lourie (1949) placed a metronome next to a headbanging child and set it to match the speed of the child's head banging, the child might have wondered, 'Is it me or the metronome that is controlling my behaviour?'" (Ross and McKay, 1979: 153)

These treatment methods, to a greater or lesser extent and in various forms, have continued to be used through the application of a number of imaginative versions of reward and punishment techniques. Current more 'modern' interventions contain similar though more subtle messages and practices which attempt to control the behaviour. These include contracts; pressures to 'promise me you'll never do it again'; attempts to find and impose causes and meanings of the behaviour; and attempts to take the behaviour away, replace it, define it, categorise it.

Indeed, one of the main facets of the theme 'who's hurting who?' is to be found in these attempts — using a variety of subtle and not so subtle means — to take the behaviour and its control away from the young people. Paradoxically such attempts can result in the young person being more hurt. This is because:

- the risk of the young person injuring themselves more severely may thereby be increased;
- the important coping aspect of the behaviour may be removed;
- the sense of purpose and identity which a young person may have developed for themselves through their self-harming may be removed; and
- the young person's ownership and control of the behaviour may be taken from them.

Often people who help can therefore be experienced as people who hurt. The result: help is confused with abuse.

Most of the unhelpful reactions and treatments the young people outlined can contribute to this confusion over who is hurting who, as well as to the perpetuation of cruelty, harm and abuse. The unhelpful reactions and responses may include:

- rejection;
- punishment;
- being forced to speak;
- being prevented from speaking (not being given space and time);
- sectioning, restraint and seclusion;
- being lectured;
- being seen as attention-seeking and manipulative;
- being moved on because of the behaviour;
- not being believed;
- being ignored.

Such interventions may reinforce both the marginalisation and the isolation of the young people and their view of themselves as bad, evil, dirty and so on. They may also increase their distrust of others and their anger, frustration and annoyance with themselves and those around them. As we have seen, because the young person is likely to self-harm in secret ('underground') the effect may be to make their behaviour potentially more dangerous — for example, by their failing to seek help when their life is at risk. In addition such interventions, particularly ones involving their being controlled, may replicate their past experiences of abuse and harm.

This confusion over the hurt and harm inflicted may be exacerbated in a number of ways. Where cruelty perpetuates itself, perceptions of victim and perpetrator of the harm can become intertwined and indistinguishable. While society and its institutions harm its members, the members will continue to harm themselves. Repeated suicide attempts and self-harming represent examples of how difficult it is to tease out why the hurt is happening, who is causing the hurt and what is actually hurting.

Sometimes the young people themselves act out a split which reflects this overall confusion over who is hurting who. Thus, as we have seen, in the act of self-harm some young people may sometimes feel that they are the ones with some power to inflict harm (on themselves); even while at other times feeling that they are the ones who are being hurt or punished. As we have also seen they may, though never outwardly communicating this, feel that their acts of self-harm are directed at those who at some point in their lives have harmed and abused them. (See Chapter 1: 'A Few Hours Break' and Chapter 5: 'A Bad Apple'.)

In fact the people around the young person (including workers, friends and family) do often appear to be more immediately affected and hurt by their behaviour, often finding it extremely difficult to witness and understand what the young person is doing to themself. It is as if the self-harm and attempted suicide threaten and harm everyone in the environment of the behaviour.

Providing help: breaking the vicious circle

Where then does all this leave the services and the workers who seek to help and support young people who harm themselves and attempt suicide? One important starting point would seem to be trying to understand this behaviour as part of the whole young person — part of their feelings, experiences, history and sense of themselves. To do this it is essential to take seriously the accounts given by young people — such as the ones detailed in this report.

What however does this mean? As has already been made clear, it is not possible to assume that solutions can be found. What follows therefore will concentrate rather on working actively with the insights provided by the young people and exploring some of the dilemmas and difficulties such an approach creates.

Repeated suicide attempts and self-harming may be a way for some young people of regulating their feelings, moods and emotions ('*to myself for myself*'). One of the interpretations on which all the young people in this study agreed was that their behaviour was in some ways helpful to them — that '*it works.*' In this sense, their attempted suicide and self-harming acted as a self-administered 'treatment' which, in spite of their situation, they had found for themselves. Their behaviour provided a response to an overwhelming event, feeling, memory which was expressed through an act which they could regulate.

Such acts however are not socially or medically sanctioned and legitimised. Ironically this may be one reason for young people adopting them and for their becoming so powerful for them. Indeed young people who repeatedly attempt suicide or self-harm are increasingly seen as problematic, troublesome and a drain on public resources.

Though workers and services may put much time and effort into supporting or treating these young people, the self-harming and suicide attempts may continue and may do so even after the young person has been treated or given support. This is because it works, at least in the short-term — when frequently everything else the young person tries or is offered seems to fail.

For the medical, psychiatric and helping establishments all this may be threatening and difficult to accept. It may also produce in workers (and in turn in young people) feelings of frustration, blame, helplessness and a desire to punish. And these in turn may help to reinforce a young person's negative feelings about themselves. This suggests that, for helpers, the key tasks then are to find ways of breaking this vicious circle; and to reduce the increased risks to a young person's health and life which it can produce.

It is not as if other ways of dealing with distress which to a greater degree are socially or medically sanctioned do not contain similar problems. Smoking, drinking, 'talking cures', psychiatric medication also carry a variety of risks — of addiction, of failing to deal with underlying issues, of merely getting rid of presenting symptoms and so on.

It is essential therefore that, in the case of attempted suicide and self-harm, workers battle against feelings that 'we can't win', or 'whatever we do is wrong' since these feed into the vicious circle which reinforces the damaging behaviour. It is important too to question, and through this to clarify, what 'failing' or 'helping' a young person who repeatedly self-harms actually means. Services and their workers often seem to need to feel that they are succeeding, doing their job and thereby helping — a position which at times may put them in conflict with a young person's felt need to harm themselves. The problem may, at least in part, exist because helping is here being measured solely in terms of stopping self-harm or preventing attempted suicide.

Sometimes, however, helping may involve having to accept that, for different young people at different times, the level and frequency of self-harm may vary and that this will be determined by the young people themselves. It may appear good that a young person has not hurt themselves or attempted suicide for a while. However, may we not also need to wonder where their troublesome underlying feelings have gone? Or for whose benefit they have stopped? Or who is feeling better because of this? Are the feelings being suppressed or are they 'on pause'? This may replicate past experiences of keeping abuse secret and could also reinforce feelings that after all no-one understands or wants to know.

Such questions suggest that services and their workers may need to recognise the limitations and dangers of focussing help for the young person on stopping their self-harming and suicide attempts as the highest priority. After all, the young person may continue to self-harm in secret and this may become a barrier to a therapeutic relationship as well as a breach of trust. Once their feelings have built up, the young person may even feel the need to harm themselves more to get the same effect as if they have self-harmed for a while. Where then is the help?

Working with the young person's account and understandings

What are the implications of accepting young people's account and understandings of their behaviour — for example their felt need to harm themselves? What is involved in working with their version of the problem and its 'solution', even when this may be uncomfortable — for example that they want it ignored, that they do not want to stop, that they do not want to 'get to the bottom of it'? Two examples illustrate this.

> *All I want is to be able to cut myself, get it bandaged, stitched if it needs it, but to carry on and live a normal life like anyone else.*

> *I don't like delving into why I do it. I find it much more easy just to cut up and (hope that) then people would shut up about it.*

In these situations, what is the helper's role ? How can workers be useful and yet not be experienced as so controlling that the support is effectively sabotaged? What place is there for supportive challenge by a worker or helper which may aid the young person's understanding of the behaviour? Whilst young people can feel intruded upon by questions which they may not be able to answer, they may also express a wish for a way into communication, to be understood.

One starting point for helpers may be to recognise the problems which arise from their own need to know 'why.' This preoccupation would seem to set in motion a process similar to the one which (despite attempts to avoid it) the researcher herself went through: searching for neat answers, conclusions and 'findings' which explained why young people self-harm or attempt suicide. Workers, counsellors and other professionals and carers may also be paralysed by this kind of pressing need to know the causes or to find the answers ('Eureka! he/she does it because ... '). Yet, as we have seen, such a focus may not always be helpful. Sometimes it may be in conflict with some of the interests and aims inherent in the very notion of 'help' in this context. Neither a worker's nor a young person's 'version' of 'why' may be better or correct — suggesting that no 'truth' may be available anyway.

Conflicts will continue between services and young people over what is appropriate behaviour, over what is and is not mentally healthy and stable, over what is wrong, acceptable and so on. These differences may be interwoven with feelings of shock and discomfort — 'how could they do that to themselves'?

However, if helpers accept a stance which acknowledges that sometimes they (and the young people) just do not know where to focus help or intervention — if they do 'accept' the behaviour and don't see it as bad or wrong — should they then simply suspend judgement and make no attempt to 'rescue' or try to stop the self-harming?

Or again, what about the pain, sadness, despair, distress, self-hate, damage, all of which are clearly so much part of a young person's life — and which presumably cannot just be ignored? Without losing sight of the distress, what seems to be crucial here is the extent to which the helper can recognise and accept all the positive associations, meanings and functions of the self-harming behaviour.

The previous chapter also indicated the often crucial conflicts generated for the young people by their own behaviour and emotions — for example, wanting other people to know/ not to know; wanting help/not wanting help. Providing 'help' may well require that these tensions are accepted and recognised. After all, the young people rarely indicated that they simply wanted their feelings, distress and behaviour to be ignored or minimised.

'Help' would thus seem to require a delicately struck balance between, for example, over-reacting and under-reacting to the behaviour. It would also need to be flexible, changeable and negotiable in order to take into account the differences and the variety of responses both within a young person and between different young people. And it would need to recognise behaviours which are important to the young person because they 'belong' to them (*'It's mine'*; *'It's to myself for myself'*). At the same time, it is important not to reinforce either their sense of isolation — of being alone — or of marginalisation — that no-one understands.

However useful such approaches may be, they still leave unanswered one other question: how do we provide a service for those young people who feel that they do not need, want or deserve it? For those, for example, who, when they want to harm themselves, would not go to a 'helping' facility because that would be tantamount to saying; 'I didn't really want to do it' or 'If I really wanted to do it then why would I want to get help?' Clearly there are no easy answers, but the question remains an important one for service-providers to consider.

Supporting workers

Finally it is important to consider the needs of workers carrying the responsibility for providing care and support for young people who self-harm or have attempted suicide. Responses here do need to recognise that the young people's behaviour has an impact on workers — that it stirs up fears and anxieties <u>in them</u>. Yet, though this need for a worker to express their frustration about the situations they meet has to be recognised, they themselves also need to acknowledge how their own negativity and criticism can reinforce a young person's view of themselves and their actual behaviour.

The dilemmas and ambiguities which the young people presented could well be reflected in the situations faced by workers because, as we have seen, they could be intrinsic to the issues with which we are dealing. It is important therefore that the support which workers receive does not impose on them hard and fast rules and 'solutions'. Rather, workers need forums in which they can express their own fears, doubts and frustrations without in their practice appearing to blame or punish the young people.

Once attention is paid to the meanings and functions of the behaviour then workers, given adequate time and space, can begin more openly to discuss the issues involved for them, support each other and demand more appropriate training and supervision. If self-harming behaviour has such strong meanings for the young people then it might well also carry powerful associations for workers. Indeed, recognising the functions which self-harm has for young people could open up questions for those working with them about how they might deal with their own distress or uncertainty — not least because such behaviour also touches a range of fundamental questions about life and death, pain, survival and identity.

It is also important to recognise that individual workers who attempt to work closely with the kind of young people's perspectives reported here could face difficulties with, and isolation and criticism from, the more established professions.

All this clearly has important implications for training and for the resources which are made available to workers.

Policy and resources

Many of the suggestions made by young people about the use of resources in the future pose a particular challenge — not only to the statutory services, but to the providers of alternative provision within the voluntary sector. This is especially the case given the current drastic underfunding of both sectors.

It is clear therefore that the extent to which planners, policy makers and others with control over resources confront these challenges will be crucial. For it will represent an important measure of how far the provocative and penetrating insights and understandings provided by the young people in this study are receiving the considered attention they deserve.

Postscript

42nd Street hopes that **Who's Hurting Who?** will stimulate thought and be a useful resource for its readers. We also hope that it will contribute to debates about suicide and self-harm and about service provision. We would be interested in hearing from readers about how this research is being used and about its contribution to developments in work practice. We would welcome readers' feedback about this. Please write to us at the address below:

42nd Street
2nd Floor, Swan Buildings
20 Swan Street
Manchester M4 5JW

REFERENCES

Appleby, Dr L. & Warner, R. (1993)
'Parasuicide: features of repetition and the implications for intervention',
Psychological Medicine, 23, 13–16

Arnold, L. (1995)
Women and Self Injury: a survey of 76 Women, Bristol Crisis Service for Women

Burstow, B. (1992)
Self Mutilation (Radical Feminist Therapy), SAGE

Cooper, D. (1970)
Psychiatry and Anti-psychiatry, Paladin

Crabtree, L.H. & Grossman, W.K. (1974)
'Administrative clarity and redefinition for an open adolescent unit',
Psychiatry, 37 (4), 350

Favazza, A.R. & Favazza, B. (1987)
Bodies Under Siege: Self Mutilation in Culture and Psychiatry,
John Hopkins University Press

Favazza, A.R. & Conterio, K. (1988)
'The plight of chronic self-mutilators', *Community Mental Health Journal*,
Vol 24

Goldacre, M. & Hawton, K. (1985)
'Repetition of self-poisoning and subsequent death in adolescents who take
overdoses', *British Journal of Psychiatry*, 146, 395–398

Harrington, R.C. & Dyer, E. (1993)
'Suicide and attempted suicide in adolescence, *Current Opinion in Psychiatry*, 6,
467–469

Hawton, K. & Catalon, J. (1987)
Attempted Suicide, Oxford University Press

Laing, R.D. (1965)
The Divided Self, Penguin

Lewis, G. & Appleby, L. (1988)
'Personality disorders', *British Journal of Psychiatry*, 153 (Nov), 702

Liebling, Helen & Chipchase, Hazel
A Pilot Study on the Problem of Self-Injurious Women in Ashworth Hospital
(unpublished and undated)

Liebling, Helen & Karup, Helen (1993)
Suicide Attempts and Self-Injury in Male Prisons: a Summary,
Institute of Criminology, Cambridge

Maris, Ronald W. (1971)
'Deviance as therapy: the paradox of the self-destructive female',
Journal of Health and Social Behaviour 12

Miller, D. (1994)
Women who Hurt Themselves, Basic Books

Owens, D. & House, A. (1994)
'General hospital services for deliberate self-harm', *Journal of the Royal College of Physicians,* 28 (4) 370–1

Pembroke, L. (1994)
Self Harm: Perspectives from Personal Experience, Survivors Speak Out

Romme, M. & Escher, S. (1993)
Accepting Voices, Mind

Ross, R.R. & McKay, H.B. (1979)
Self Mutilation, Lexington Books

Rygnestad, T. (1988)
'A prospective five-year follow-up study of self-poisoned patients',
Acta Psychiatricia Scandinavica, 77 (3), 328–31

Tantam, D. & Whittaker, J. (1992)
'Personality disorder and self-wounding', *British Journal of Psychiatry,* 161, 451–464

Threshold Newsletter (1995)
Initiative for Women and Mental Health, Brighton

APPENDIX

Suicide/Self-harm Research Project Initial Interview Format

1) Introduction:

- Aims and focus of interview
- Explain interview format
- Length of interview — one to two hours
- Possible break if necessary
- Explain ethos of interview
- Introduce/outline sections

2) Ground rules/Contract:

- Confidentiality
- Don't necessarily need clear answers
- Honest as possible
- Time to think
- O.K to ask for clarification
- O.K to 'pass' on questions
- Can terminate interview if nessesary
- Will be able to see transcript of interview and final report

3) Interview Questions

4) Ending the Interview

- To discuss further contact
- To discuss what to do with any 'issues' that have arisen during interview
- Feedback

Interview Questions/Topic Areas

Introductory Questions/Setting the scene

1 Could you tell a bit about yourself, particularly in relation to any suicide attempts you have made and any times where you have harmed yourself?

2 Would you see yourself as 'repeatedly' or even 'regularly' attempting suicide and/or harming yourself? (Discuss definitions) — Could you tell me how you would describe it?

3 Could you tell me something about what it's like to want to hurt yourself?

4 Could you tell me about what part your suicide attempts and/or self-harm has played in your life?

Suicide/Self-harm Distinction

5 Could you tell me any differences between when you self-harm (use young people's words) to when you attempt suicide? OR What do you think the difference is between when young people self-harm and when they attempt suicide?

6 Some people say that attempting suicide is about not wanting to live anymore and self-harm is about wanting to live/survive/cope.
   • What do you think about this?
   • How does this fit your experience?

Development of Repetition

7 Can you identify the first time that you harmed yourself or attempted suicide. Keep in mind that this may include something that seemed at the time to be an 'accident'.

8 Could you recall some of the circumstances around this event?
   • Your situation at the time
   • The 'purpose' of the act
   • The response you received

9 Could you tell me about how you think your self-harm and/or suicide attempts developed and continued?

10 What do you think may be some of the difference between young people who attempt suicide/self-harm once or maybe a couple of times and young people who 'repeatedly' do it?

11 Do you have any opinions about other young people who 'repeatedly' attempt suicide and/or self-harm? (Anything you have noticed/observed as an 'outsider'?)

Identifying Causes/Factors

12 What do you think may be some of the reasons that young people repeatedly self-harm and/or attempt suicide?

13 Could you identify any particular experiences or events in you life — things maybe that have happened to you — which may be related to your suicide attempts and/or self-harm?

14 Although not everybody who repeatedly attempts suicide and/or self-harms has been abused in childhood there does appear to be a very strong link between childhod physical and sexual abuse and repeated suicide attempts/self-harm. What do you think?

15 It often appears that when people are in places where they feel 'controlled' such as prisons, secure units, hospitals, certain family environments etc. they are more likely to attempt suicide/self-harm.
   • How does this relate to your experience?

Reactions/Responses

16 A common comment people make when coming across someone who has attempted suicide and/or self-harmed 'repeatedly'/on a number of occasions is that they are 'attention-seeking'. What would you say about this?

17 Another comment is that the person is 'manipulative'; that they are trying to manipulate others into doing what they want. What are your thoughts about this?

18 How do you think professionals or other workers see you particularly in relation to your suicide attempts and/or self-harm?

19 Can you tell me about some of the reactions of people when you have attempted suicide and/or self-harmed?

20 a) What labels/diagnoses/names are you aware of being given in reference to your behaviour?
   b) Have you found this helpful?
   c) Has it had any effect on you?

21 How have you been able to challenge any stereotypes or 'bad' attitudes and reactions?

Services

22 Do you have any thoughts or things to say about any services you are or were involved with e.g. hospitals, day centres, workers, psychiatrists, projects (including 42nd Street).

23 Can you imagine a place or service where you could go either when you feel suicidal/self-harming, or to go when you have just attempted suicide/self-harmed. What would it be like?

24 Do you think that you would like to be able to 'give up' attempting suicide/self-harming?

25 If yes, can you imagine what sort of support you may need, or what sort of place you would need to be where you may feel safe enough to begin to give it up?
   • What sort of changes do you think would need to be made, to your situation, your life, in order for this to be able to happen?

Benefits of Suicide/Self-harm

26 Some people say that attempting suicide and/or self-harming can become like a way of communicating or even a language to say things which the person cannot put into words. What are your thoughts on this? (Also in relation to this interview).

27 Do you think that in some ways your suicide attempts and/or self-harm have been therapeutic, that is, in some ways helpful to yourself and your situation?
   • In what ways? Could you take me through this?

Anything else?

   • Is there anything else you would like to say which we have not covered?
   • Any questions?
   • Feedback on interview and questions e.g. Would it have been useful to have had questions before interview?